This present collection of writings by Lewis Carroll — the King of "Nonsense Literature" — is particularly opportune. Most, if not all, the matter in it will be new to the present generation; some of it, indeed, has never appeared in print before.

Thirty-three selections of verse and prose are here to amuse, delight and, sometimes, confound the reader. In addition, there is a chapter reproducing the best Lewis Carroll anecdotes by him and about him, for no book of this kind would be complete without reference to his inimitable talent as a raconteur.

The present volume was edited by Langford Reed, who has contributed a valuable biographical foreword and interesting annotations to the various selections.

H. M. Bateman's illustrations are perfectly in spirit with the topsy-turvy imagination of the author and add considerably to the general merriment.

FURTHER NONSENSE VERSE AND PROSE

BY

LEWIS CARROLL, pseud.
(EDITED BY LANGFORD REED)

ILLUSTRATED BY
H. M. BATEMAN

D. APPLETON AND COMPANY
NEW YORK ✿ ✿ ✿ MCMXXVI

248454

CONTENTS

Contents

FOREWORD

This present collection of writings by Lewis Carroll—the King of "Nonsense Literature"—is particularly opportune. Most, if not all, the matter in it will be new to the present generation; some of it, indeed, has never appeared in print before.

Apart from other material, more than one hundred and fifty letters have been examined. Lewis Carroll was a prolific correspondent, and his letters, especially to his child friends, reflected his joyous personality and characteristic humour in no uncommon degree. In this connection, and for some of the biographical details in his introduction, the editor wishes to acknowledge his indebtedness to Mr. Stuart Dodgson Collingwood's "Life and Letters of Lewis Carroll" (a fascinating book long out of print), and to Miss Vera Beringer, Mrs. Barclay, Mrs. Spens, and Mrs. Morton (formerly the three little Miss Bowmans), four ladies who, when children, were among the most intimate of Lewis Carroll's juvenile comrades. The courtesy of the proprietors of "The Whitby Gazette" in giving permission for the inclusion of "The Lady of the Ladle" and "Wilhelm von Schmitz" must be acknowledged.

THE REAL LEWIS CARROLL

Lewis Carroll's real name, as most of his adult admirers are aware, was Charles Lutwidge Dodgson, and he was born on January 27, 1832, in the Cheshire village of Daresbury, where his father was the local parson.

In this secluded hamlet young Dodgson spent the first eleven years of his life, and in his quaint diversions and hobbies gave promise of the whimsical and bizarre genius which was destined to make him famous.

His biographer has left it on record that he made pets of snails and other queer creatures, and endeavoured to encourage organised warfare among insects by supplying them with pieces of stick with which they might fight, if so disposed.

He also showed early signs of mathematical and scientific talent which, if not rare enough to make the name of Charles Lutwidge Dodgson as imperishably and as internationally illustrious as that of Lewis Carroll, rendered it well known in his own generation among his own countrymen, and proved that he was one of those singular geniuses whom, in his own quaint phraseology, he would have described as a "portmanteau" man—that is to say, one man packed with several individualities!

Of the delightful surroundings of his birthplace he has left the following impression in his serious poem, "The Three Sunsets" (first published in "All the Year Round" in 1860):

> I watch the drowsy night expire,
> And Fancy paints at my desire
> Her magic pictures in the fire.
> An island farm, 'midst seas of corn
> Swayed by the wandering breath of morn,
> The happy spot where I was born.

In 1843 the Rev. Mr. Dodgson became rector of Croft, a Durham village near Darlington, with a quaint old church which contains a Norman porch and an elaborate covered-in pew resembling a four-post bedstead. Soon after the transference he was appointed examining chaplain to the Bishop of Ripon, and later became Archdeacon of Richmond (Yorkshire), and one of the Canons of Ripon Cathedral.

"Young Dodgson at this time," says the authority already quoted, "was very fond of inventing games for the amusement of his brothers and sisters; he constructed a home-made train out of a wheelbarrow, a barrel, and a small truck, which used to convey passengers from one 'station' in the rectory gardens to another. At each of these stations there was a refreshment room, and the passengers had to purchase tickets from him before they could enjoy the ride. The boy was also a clever conjuror, and arrayed in a brown wig and a long white robe, used to cause no little wonder to his audience by his sleight of hand tricks. With the assistance of various members of the family and the village carpenter he made a troupe of marionettes and a small theatre for them to act in. He wrote all the plays himself and he was very clever at manipulating the innumerable strings by which the movements of his puppets were regulated."

A Prophecy That Came True

It was in 1844, at the mature age of twelve, when he was a pupil at Richmond School, that he wrote his first story. It was called "The Unknown One," and appeared in the school magazine.

That the headmaster anticipated that his young pupil might one day astonish the world may be gathered by the following extract from his first report upon him:

"I do not hesitate to express my opinion that he possesses, along with other and excellent natural endowments, a very uncommon share of genius; he is capable of acquirements and knowledge far beyond his years, while his reason is so clear and so zealous of error, that he will not rest satisfied without a most exact solution of whatever appears to him obscure. You may fairly anticipate for him a bright career."

At the age of fourteen Charles was sent to Rugby School, becoming a pupil a few years after the death of the great Dr. Arnold, immortalised in "Tom Brown's Schooldays." The headmaster was

Dr. A. C. Tait, who afterwards became Archbishop of Canterbury. His opinion of his pupil's ability was thus expressed in a letter to Archdeacon Dodgson:

"I must not allow your son to leave school without expressing to you the very high opinion I entertain of him. His mathematical knowledge is great for his age, and I doubt not he will do himself credit in classics; his examination for the Divinity Prize was one of the most creditable exhibitions I have ever seen."

Young Dodgson's literary activities appear to have definitely commenced about the year 1845, when the first of a series of amateur magazines, which he edited during the holidays for the benefit of the inmates of Croft Rectory made its appearance. The most ambitious of these home-made journals was "The Rectory Umbrella," for which, in addition to editing, he wrote most of the matter and made all the illustrations.

In the spring of 1850 he matriculated, and in January, 1851, following in the footsteps of his father, he became a student at Christ Church College, Oxford, and commenced a personal association with it which lasted until the day of his death, forty-seven years later. Scholastic honours and distinctions were his almost from the very first, for he soon won a Boulter Scholarship and obtained First Class Honours in Mathematics and Second in Classical Moderations. The degrees of Bachelor of Arts and Master of Arts followed.

In 1853, during a stay at Ripon, he met a singular person who identified with remarkable accuracy the qualities and characteristics which were to make him famous. This was a Miss Anderson, who professed to have clairvoyant powers, and by merely holding a folded paper containing writing by a person unknown to her to be able to describe his or her character. This was her delineation of young Dodgson's:

"Very clever head, a great deal of imitation; he would make a good actor; diffident; rather shy in general society; comes out in the home circle; rather obstinate, very clever; a great deal of concentration; very affectionate; a great deal of wit and humour; not much faculty for remembering events; fond of deep reading; imaginative; fond of reading poetry; may compose."

The following year he contributed the poem and short story to "The Whitby Gazette" which are included in this present volume.

His love of the theatre alluded to by the psychical lady was an early one. In his diary for June 22, 1853, he thus refers to an evening spent at the Princess's Theatre, London:

"Then came the great play 'Henry VIII.,' the greatest theatrical treat I have ever had or expect to have. I had no idea that anything so superb as the scenery and dresses was ever to be seen on the stage. Kean was magnificent as Cardinal Wolsey, Mrs. Kean a worthy successor to Mrs. Siddons as Queen Catherine, and all the accessories without exception were good—but oh, that exquisite vision of Queen Catherine! I almost held my breath to watch, the illusion is perfect, and I felt as if in a dream the whole time it lasted. It was like a delicious reverie or most beautiful poetry. This is the true end and object of acting—to raise the mind above itself and out of its petty cares."

Another entry is full of the diffidence about himself and his work which was characteristic of the man. It read as follows:

"I am sitting alone in my bedroom this last night of the old year (1857) waiting for midnight. It has been the most eventful year of my life: I began it as a poor bachelor student, with no definite plans or expectations; I end it as a master and tutor in Christ Church, with an income of more than £300 a year, and the course of mathematical tuition marked out by God's providence for at least some years to come. Great mercies, great failings, time lost, talent misapplied—such has been the past year."

At Christmas he became the editor of a college publication called "College Rhymes," in which first appeared "A Sea Dirge" and

"My Fancy," both of which are included in this present volume. About the same period he contributed several poems to "The Comic Times," and later to "The Train." Edmund Yates, the editor of both publications, expressed the warmest appreciation of his work.

THE "BIRTH" OF "LEWIS CARROLL"

It was during young Dodgson's association with the latter journal that the pseudonym, which is to-day world-famous, originated. It was selected by Edmund Yates from the names Edgar Cuthwellis,* Edgar W. C. Westhall, Louis Carroll, and Lewis Carroll. The first two were formed from letters of his Christian names, Charles Lutwidge; the others are merely variant forms of them. Thus Lewis is developed from Ludovicus and Ludovicus from Luteridge, while Charles develops into Carolus and thence to Carroll.

The first effort from his pen to which the new pseudonym was appended was "The Path of Roses," a serious poem which appeared in "The Train" in 1856.

Mr. Dodgson was ordained a deacon of the Church of England in 1861, but never undertook regular duties as a priest, although he preached occasionally at the University Church and elsewhere. Despite the slight stammer which marred his diction his sermons— models of earnestness, lucidity, and reasoning—were always impressive, especially those on the subject of Eternal Punishment, in which devilish and anti-Christian doctrines he was, of course an emphatic disbeliever.

His literary activities and personal charm gained him the friendship of eminent writers in various fields of artistic and professional endeavour, including Tennyson, Ruskin, Thackeray, the Rossetti Family, Tom Taylor the dramatist (author of "Still Waters Run

* Actually used by Mr. Dodgson in his story, "The Legend of Scotland," included in this volume.

6

Deep," etc.), Frank Smedley (author of that admirable novel "Frank Fairleigh"), Stuart Calverley, Coventry Patmore, Mrs. Charlotte the novelist, Millais, Holman Hunt, Val Prinsep, Watts, the Terry family, Lord Salisbury, the Bishop of Oxford, Canon King (afterwards Bishop of Lincoln), Canon Liddon, Dr. Scott (Dean of Rochester), Dr. Liddell (Dean of Christ Church), Professor Faraday, Mr. Justice Denman, Sir George Baden-Powell, Mr. Frederick Harrison, etc.

Most of these distinguished people were photographed by him, for this man of many talents had a flair for artistic photography which undoubtedly would have made him successful as a professional photographer had he been compelled to depend upon it for a living. Photographing from life, particularly photographing children, was, indeed, his principal hobby, and in his rooms at Christ Church he kept a large and varied assortment of fancy costumes in which to attire his little friends for picturesque effect.

The Beginning of "Alice"

It was on July 4, 1862, that there occurred that epochal expedition up the river to Godstow with the three small daughters of Dr. Liddell, Dean of Christ Church, which was destined to have such important and far-reaching results. The first inception of the resultant masterpiece has been charmingly described in the beautiful verses which preface it:

> All in the golden afternoon
>   Full leisurely we glide,
> For both our oars, with little skill,
>   By little arms are plied.
> While little hands make vain pretence
>   Our wanderings to guide.
>
> Ah, cruel three!   In such an hour
>   Beneath such dreamy weather
> To beg a tale of breath too weak
>   To stir the tiniest feather!
> Yet what can one poor voice avail
>   Against three tongues together?
>
> Imperious Prima flashes forth
>   Her edict "to begin it"—
> In gentler tone Secunda hopes
>   "There will be nonsense in it!"—
> While Tertia interrupts the tale
>   Not *more* than once a minute.
>
> Anon, to sudden silence won,
>   In fancy they pursue

The Beginning of "Alice"

The dream-child moving through a land
    Of wonders wild and new.
In friendly chat with bird or beast—
    And half believe it true.

And even, as the story drained
    The wells of fancy dry,
And faintly strove that weary one
    To put the subject by,
"The rest next time"—"It *is* next time!"
    The happy voices cry.

Thus grew the tale of Wonderland:
    Thus slowly, one by one,
Its quaint events were hammered out—
    And now the tale is done,
And home we steer, a merry crew,
    Beneath the setting sun.

Alice! a childish story take,
    And with a gentle hand
Lay it where childhood's dreams are twined
    In Memory's mystic band,
Like pilgrim's wither'd wreath of flowers
    Pluck'd in a far-off land.

If the final verse is not proof enough that sweet Alice Liddell was Lewis Carroll's favourite of the three, and that for *her* he fashioned his immortal fantasy, the opening verses from the exquisite poem which precedes the sequel to the story, "Alice through the Looking Glass," will dispel all doubt:

Child of the pure unclouded brow
    And dreaming eyes of wonder!
Though time be fleet and I and thou
    Are half a life asunder,
Thy loving smile will surely hail
    The love gift of a fairy-tale.

I have not seen thy sunny face,
 Nor heard thy silver laughter;
No thought of me shall find a place
 In thy young life's hereafter—
Enough that now thou wilt not fail
 To listen to my fairy-tale.

A tale begun in other days,
 When summer suns were glowing—
A simple chime that served to time
 The rhythm of our rowing—
Whose echoes live in memory yet,
 Though envious years would say "forget."

It is pleasant to reflect that Lewis Carroll was wrong in his assumption that his little comrade would forget him. She remained his lifelong friend, and many years after the trip to Godstow, when she had become Mrs. Reginald Hargreaves, she wrote the following account of the scene:

"I believe the beginning of 'Alice' was told me one summer afternoon when the sun was so hot that we had landed in the meadows down the river, deserting the boat to take refuge in the only bit of shade to be found, which was under a new-made hay-rick. Here from all three came the old petition of 'Tell us a story,' and so began the ever-delightful tale. Sometimes to tease us— perhaps being really tired—Mr. Dodgson would stop suddenly and say, 'And that's all till next time.' 'Ah, but it is next time,' would be the exclamation from all three; and after some persuasion the story would start afresh. Another day, perhaps, the story would begin in the boat, and Mr. Dodgson, in the middle of telling a thrilling adventure, would pretend to go fast asleep, to our great dismay. . . ."

The original title of the story, which its creator took the trouble to write out in manuscript and have specially bound for the living

Alice, was "Alice's Adventures Underground"; later it became "Alice's Hour in Elfland." It was not until June 18, 1864, that its author finally decided upon "Alice's Adventures in Wonderland," and it was a year later before it was published. He had no thought of publication at first, and it was his friend Mr. George Macdonald who persuaded him to submit the story to Messrs. Macmillan, who immediately appreciated its value.

Few books have met with such unequivocal praise from the critics and such instantaneous favour from the public, and the writer of these notes feels sure that in any public enquiry conducted into the popularity of children's books to-day, either in Great Britain or America, "Alice in Wonderland" would come at easy first. His own little daughter, Joan, ætat. nine, never tires of the wonderful adventures, and thinks it "the very best story in the world," and this opinion is probably typical of nine children out of ten.

The story has been translated into French, German, Italian, and Dutch—tasks which the peculiarly Anglo-Saxon character of its appeal must have rendered very difficult.

Four years after the publication of his masterpiece there appeared its author's collection of poems grave and gay, known under the general title of "Phantasmagoria," followed two years later by "Alice through the Looking Glass."

Soon after this he commenced to work out the story of "Sylvie and Bruno," and on the last night of 1872 related a great deal of it to several children, including Princess Alice, who were members of a party at Hatfield, where Mr. Dodgson was the guest of Lord Salisbury.

In 1871 appeared his "Notes by an Oxford Chiel," a collection of whimsical papers dealing with Oxford controversies; and in March, 1879, "The Hunting of the Snark" was published. According to its creator, the first idea for the whole poem was suggested by its last line, "For the Snark *was* a Boojum, you see," which came into his mind, apparently without reason, while he was enjoying a country walk. Many of his admirers have contended that "The Hunting of the Snark" is an allegory, but Lewis Carroll himself always declared it had no meaning at all, which, however, is very different from saying it had no point, for the meticulous skill with which each effect is achieved shows the master-hand throughout.

All this time Mr. Dodgson, in addition to his professional duties, was writing mathematical and technical and other serious works, for which he was responsible for more than a dozen books alone, including "Euclid and his Modern Rivals" (1882), which ran into eight editions.

INVENTOR OF CROSS WORD PUZZLES

In addition, he invented many ingenious table games and puzzles, and an examination of some of these has suggested to the editor that in all probability he was the real inventor of "Cross Word Puzzles."

As, however, this introduction is concerned principally with the humorous literary achievements and characteristics of Lewis Carroll, anything more than a passing reference to matters outside that scope would be inappropriate, particularly since time has to a great extent already endorsed the uncompromising prophecy which appeared at the end of a wonderful laudation of Lewis Carroll in "The National Review" a few days after his death, which stated: "Future generations will not waste a single thought upon the Rev. C. L. Dodgson."

In 1855 appeared "A Tangled Tale," in which Mr. Carroll successfully combined mathematics and nonsense in a series of ingenious problems; and at the end of 1889 "Sylvie and Bruno," on which he had been engaged for several years. "Sylvie and Bruno Concluded" followed in 1893.

Neither of these stories achieved anything approaching the success of the "Alice" books or "The Hunting of the Snark," for in them he made the mistake of endeavouring to combine a fairy-tale with a serious and controversial novel full of religious and political arguments; and commendable though this may have been from the Christian and ethical standpoint, it made neither for unity nor clarity. Mingled with this extraneous matter, however, is some delightful nonsense, equal to anything in the "Alice" books, particularly in respect of the Mad Gardener and his weird optic delusions; while his heroine, Sylvie, is an idealistic and entrancing creature who appeals to the very best that is in humanity, which brings me to the question: "What is it precisely which delights and amuses us in Lewis Carroll's fantasies?"

It is a difficult question to answer, for his humour is of that rare quality that is intangible and, so to speak, incomplete. It approximates to that of Shakespeare in "A Midsummer Night's Dream" and Barrie in "Peter Pan." I can think of no others. His quaint conversations and fantastic scenes abound in ideas that seem to vanish before we can quite grasp them—like the Cheshire Cat, leaving only the smile behind, or like our conception of his immortal Snark, that was not strictly a Snark because it was a Boojum! He never makes the mistake of less responsible and less "designing" writers of satiating us with good things; on completing a story by him we are always left with the impression that, had he felt so disposed, he could have added another chapter or two as alluring as the previous matter. And, more than any other writer, he has fathomed the mysterious depths of childhood that lie within us— even within the hearts of those of us who are but children of a longer growth. It is these various propensities, together with his command of language and "technique"—noticeable even when his

13

imagination and fancy run at their most preposterous riot—which surely provide the answer to the question as to what are the constituent factors responsible for Lewis Carroll's popularity; and I disagree emphatically with the opinion in a recent anthology compiled by a distinguished and charming foreign writer who considers that "the poetry of nonsense as Carroll understood it is entirely irresponsible, and the main point about it is that there is no point."

This gentleman has, I venture to think, made the mistake of attempting to regard Lewis Carroll from a literal point of view (which, of course, cannot be done) instead of from a literary one, for such a description, if true, would reduce his work to the level of the "eenar deenar dinar doe" gibberish of the nursery, or to the unconscious nonsense babblings of idiocy. To carry the argument a step further, any combination of words picked haphazard from the dictionary might be called a nonsense story!

The present writer agrees that legitimate Nonsense Verse and Prose appears to be entirely irresponsible, but surely that is one of the phrases of paradox which make the fantasies of Carroll and Barrie so elusive and so charming to every individual between seven and seventy who retains anything of the divine spark of childhood within his heart, whether he realises the reason for his enchantment or not.

Lewis Carroll's Technique

Actually the Nonsense writings of Lewis Carroll are a highly technical form of conscious and responsible humour, which, when analysed, are found to contain plot (or "idea"), achievements, climax, and, in the case of his poems, rhyme and rhythm. "Jabberwocky" offers excellent proof of this. Rhyme and rhythm, indeed, are absolutely essential to good Nonsense Verse, which the further removed it is from rules of sense must conform the more closely to rules of sound. It is these factors and the others mentioned in conjunction with them which render Nonsense Poetry so superior to the nonsense rhymes of the nursery and the folk song, including the sea chanty. One type is Nonsense, the other D—— Nonsense. Then, of course, there is sheer Nonsense; but as this is principally confined to the speeches and writings of politicians, we need not enlarge on that aspect of the question here.

So responsible and conscious a literary jester was Lewis Carroll that it is doubtful if there has ever been a more meticulous precisian in the use and intentional misuse of words, including those coined by himself. Every word, every comma, had to be printed exactly as he had planned in his development of the spontaneous idea upon which the particular story or poem was based, and no author took more trouble to ensure that the illustrations to his books exactly corresponded to his conception of the subject. He would send back drawings again and again, no matter how distinguished the artist might be, until some little defect in suggestion, as he saw it, was remedied, and was equally fastidious with regard to the style in which his books were produced. Thus, "Sylvie and Bruno Concluded" appears on announcement which states:

"For over twenty-five years I have made it my chief object, with regard to my books, that they should be of the best workmanship obtainable at the price. And I am deeply annoyed to find that the last issue of 'Through the Looking Glass,' consisting of the Sixtieth Thousand, has been put on sale without its being noticed that most of the pictures have failed so much in the printing as to make the book not worth buying. I request all holders of copies to send them to Messrs. ——— with their names and addresses, and copies of the new issue shall be sent them in exchange."

Undoubtedly he has his limitations, particularly in his best and most characteristic work. This may appear paradoxical, but the writer of these notes is strongly of the opinion that one of the most fascinating qualities about Lewis Carroll's work is that its popularity is never likely to be universal. His humour is essentially "Anglo-Saxon," and its "psychology" also, which explains why Carroll's "immortality" as a genius is founded on British and American appreciation, and why the various foreign translations of his works were comparative failures. A remarkable endorsement of the American popularity of his works appeared on July 14th, this year, in the London papers. The account in "The Daily News" read as follows:

"In the handbook of the American students who will be touring England this summer, issued by the National Union of Students, a number of books are recommended as calculated to give young Americans 'some comprehension of English life and thought.'

"Among them I observe: 'Alice in Wonderland,' 'Pride and Prejudice,' Chesterton's 'The Flying Inn,' 'The Forsyte Saga,' 'Tess of the d'Urbervilles,' 'A Shropshire Lad,' 'Major Barbara,' and 'Man and Superman.'"

THE GOLDEN AGE OF LITERATURE

It may be contended of Lewis Carroll (as of all the Victorian writers), that he lived in the "golden age" in respect of opportunity for literary achievement. In his day, life flowed on smoothly and uneventfully for the great majority of people. Our fathers laboured and loved, or did the reverse, with a freedom from worry and responsibility that may not have been very stimulating, but must have been decidedly comfortable. Those were the days when "gaunt tragedy," transpontine melodrama, and "crescendos" of horror and gloom were more popular than humour; indeed, thoughtful people turned towards them as a relief and "inspiration" when compared with the uneventful and prosaic tenor of life. It says much, therefore, for Lewis Carroll's unique genius that he was able to achieve immediate fame in an altogether different medium.

It must be admitted that the argument that his love for children was partial, inasmuch as boys were excluded from it, rests upon a great deal of truth. Though essentially a manly man himself, who did not fear to use his fists at school against attempted aggression by other boys, or in defence of the weak, he has left it on record that he did not understand boys, and felt shy in their presence, while the only literary tribute he paid to boy-nature was in his creation of "Bruno." Nor has the compiler of this volume been able to discover any record of friendship between him and a small member of his own sex.

The fact that he had eight sisters and only two brothers may have contributed something to this partiality, which, however, is a very natural one. Nearly all normal men prefer little girls to little boys, just as most women would prefer to make a pet of one of the latter, rather than of a miniature specimen of their own adorable sex. Is it not proverbial that the small daughter is "daddy's darling," and the small son mother's? And if Lewis Carroll has typified this characteristic in his idealistic "Alice," has not a famous woman writer on the other side of the Atlantic made equivalent representation in her "Little Lord Fauntleroy"?

In his natural preference for the feminine side of humanity it is remarkable that Lewis Carroll apparently never had a love affair. He does not seem to have had any flirtations even, although he must have known many charming young ladies whose friendship he had first gained as children. How emphatic was his resolve to maintain his bachelor freedom may be gathered from the following extract from a letter, written when he was fifty-two years old, to an old college friend: "So you have been for twelve years a married man, while I am still a lonely old bachelor! And mean to keep so for the matter of that. College life is by no means an unmixed misery, though married life has no doubt many charms to which I am a stranger."

Mr. Dodgson died at Guildford on January 14, 1898, following a few days' illness from influenza, which had attacked him at his sister's house, "The Chestnuts," where, in accordance with his usual custom, he had gone to spend Christmas. He was hard at work at the time upon the second volume of his "Symbolic Logic."

He was buried in the old portion of Guildford Cemetery, and on June 14th of the present year the writer of these notes and his wife visited the spot. A plain white cross and a triple pediment, "erected in loving memory by his brothers and sisters," record that—

CHARLES LUTWIDGE DODGSON

(LEWIS CARROLL)

Fell asleep, January 14, 1898,

Age 65 years,

together with the following inscriptions, singularly appropriate to one whose whole life was one of service:

"Where I am, there shall also My servant be."

"His servants shall serve Him."

"Father, in Thy gracious keeping
Leave we now Thy servant sleeping."

A grave as modest and unpretentious as the man himself, surmounted by no "immortelles," or other examples of the undertaker's art, as was the case, at the time of our visit, with adjacent graves. Nature, however, has paid a more graceful tribute than any which could be made by the hand of man. A drooping and beautiful yew tree stands sentinel at the head of the tomb, its foliage sheltering it lovingly from storms and heat, and its trunk entwined with little heart-shaped ivy leaves, just as the genius sleeping there attracted the hearts of little children a generation ago and his works will continue to do for all time.

On the other side the white blossoms of a verdant syringa were scattering themselves across the foot of the grave as if in votive offering to the white spirit which once tenanted the mortal reliquiæ within it.

The cemetery is beautifully situated on the slopes of that famous and picturesque Surrey hill known as "The Hog's Back," and though the steep and toilsome ascent must be very trying to mourners who make it on foot, of such travail is your true pilgrimage made. Few if any of the people of Guildford make it for the purpose of visiting the last resting-place of Lewis Carroll, however. Indeed, it seems extremely improbable that more than a tiny minority of them are aware that he is buried there.

Three local ladies of whom we made enquiries in the cemetery were astonished when we informed them that it contained the last resting-place of the author of "Alice in Wonderland," and listened with the greatest interest to a discursive and aged sexton whom we contrived to "unearth," who had not only buried him, but had been acquainted with him in life. He told us that not many people visited the grave, but those that did were nearly all Americans! How surprised some of these Transatlantic enthusiasts must be when they find that "The Chestnuts," where Lewis Carroll died and spent so much of his time during the last twenty years or so of his life, is without the usual plaque to distinguish it as a habitation of the Great!

They do these things better in Copenhagen, where, it seems, a Hans Christian Andersen Memorial Park has been planned, which is to contain statues of the Danish author's most charming char-

19

acters, set among leafy bowers and flower gardens, the latter to be tended by teams of children from the various Council Schools.

Besides, such a memorial plaque on "The Chestnuts" would be a very small tribute materially, and yet as a mark of spiritual recognition it would be sufficient. Assuredly Lewis Carroll would not wish for more, for the fact that his works will never be forgotten he would consider remembrance enough.

All the same, there is something fine and exultant in the feeling which inspires people to pay reverence to one who by achieving honour and fame himself has brought honour and fame to his country, whether the "departed" be symbolical of "collective achievement," as in the case of the "unknown soldier," or whether he be a great poet, writer, inventor, scientist, general, king or president, or even a politician or commercial magnate.

LANGFORD REED.

HAMPSTEAD,
LONDON.

FURTHER NONSENSE
VERSE AND PROSE

THE LADY OF THE LADLE *

(From "The Whitby Gazette" of August 31, 1854)

The Youth at Eve had drunk his fill,
Where stands the "Royal" on the Hill,
And long his mid-day stroll had made,
On the so called "Marine Parade"—

* It has given the editor much pleasure to "discover" this poem and the story "Wilhelm von Schmitz" on p. 57, for since their original appearance in print seventy-two years ago neither has been published, or even

(Meant, I presume, for Seamen brave,
Whose "march is on the Mountain wave";
'Twere just the bathing-place for him
Who stays on land till he can swim—)
And he had strayed into the Town,
And paced each alley up and down,
Where still so narrow grew the way,
The very houses seemed to say,
Nodding to friends across the Street,
"One struggle more and we shall meet."
And he had scaled that wondrous stair
That soars from earth to upper air
Where rich and poor alike must climb,
And walk the treadmill for a time.
That morning he had dressed with care,
And put Pomatum in his hair;
He was, the loungers all agreed,
A very heavy swell indeed:
Men thought him, as he swaggered by,
Some scion of nobility,

quoted, and it is extremely doubtful whether more than two or three people know of their existence. So that if not "new and unpublished matter by
Lewis Carroll" in fact, they are certainly so in effect—so far as every one
younger than eighty is concerned! Mr. Dodgson composed them during
the Oxford Long Vacation of 1854, which he spent at Whitby reading for
Mathematics. He stayed at 5, East Terrace, from July 20th to September
21st. He was twenty-two at the time, and this early work from his pen,
although somewhat periphrastic, gives promise, in its appreciation of the
preposterous and the calculated precision of its phraseology, of the genius
which was destined to make the name of Lewis Carroll immortal. The
"Hilda" and the "Goliath" were local pleasure craft of the period, and
the "wondrous stair" refers presumably to that steep and picturesque ascent
known as "Jacob's Ladder," which is still a Whitby wonder.

The Lady of the Ladle

And never dreamed, so cold his look,
That he had loved—and loved a Cook.
Upon the beach he stood and sighed,
Unheedful of the treacherous tide;
Thus sang he to the listening main,
And soothed his sorrow with the strain!

CORONACH

"She is gone by the Hilda,
  She is lost unto Whitby,
And her name is Matilda,
  Which my heart it was smit by;
Tho' I take the Goliah,
  I learn to my sorrow
That 'it won't,' says the crier,
  'Be off till to-morrow.'

"She called me her 'Neddy,'
  (Tho' there mayn't be much in it,)
And I should have been ready,
  If she'd waited a minute;
I was following behind her,
  When, if you recollect, I
Merely ran back to find a
  Gold pin for my neck-tie.

"Rich dresser of suit!
  Prime hand at a sausage!
I have lost thee, I rue it,
  And my fare for the passage!
Perhaps *she* thinks it funny,
  Aboard of the Hilda,
But I've lost purse and money,
  And thee, oh, my 'Tilda!"

24

Coronach

His pin of gold the youth undid
And in his waistcoat-pocket hid,
Then gently folded hand in hand,
And dropped asleep upon the sand.

B. B.*

* What these initials stand for the editor nas not the vaguest notion. It was not until nearly two years after the publication of the above verses that Mr. Dodgson used the pseudonym of "Lewis Carroll," which he appended to his poem, "The Path of Roses," published in "The Train" in May, 1856.

LAYS OF SORROW

(From "The Rectory Umbrella,"* 1849-50
with footnotes by the author)

The day was wet, the rain fell souse
    Like jars of strawberry jam,† a
Sound was heard in the old hen house,
    A beating of a hammer.
Of stalwart form, and visage warm,
    Two youths were seen within it,
Splitting up an old tree into perches for their poultry
    At a hundred strokes a minute.‡

The work is done, the hen has taken
    Possession of her nest and eggs,
Without a thought of eggs and bacon,§
    (Or I am very much mistaken)
    She turns over each shell,
    To be sure that all's well,
    Looks into the straw
    To see there's no flaw,

*This was one of the best of the many "family" magazines with the editing of which young Dodgson used to amuse himself during his holidays. The whole of the matter was written in manuscript, in the neat and formal handwriting characteristic of him. He was about seventeen years old at the time he composed this poem, in which the talent for nonsense rhyming of the future creator of the inimitable "Jabberwocky" is already suggested.

†*I.e.*, the jam without the jars; observe the beauty of this rhyme.

‡At the rate of a stroke and two-thirds in a second.

§Unless the hen was a poacher, which is unlikely.

26

Goes once round the house, *
    Half afraid of a mouse,
    Then sinks calmly to rest
    On the top of her nest,
First doubling up each of her legs.

Time rolled away, and so did every shell,
    "Small by degrees and beautifully less,"
As the sage mother with a powerful spell †
    Forced each in turn its contents to "express," ‡
But ah! "imperfect is expression,"
    Some poet said, I don't care who,
If you want to know you must go elsewhere,
    One fact I can tell, if you're willing to hear,
He never attended a Parliament Session,
    For I'm sure that if he had ever been there,
Full quickly would he have changed his ideas,
    With the hissings, the hootings, the groans and the cheers
And as to his name it is pretty clear
    That is wasn't me and it wasn't you!

And so it fell upon a day,
    (That is, it never rose again,)
A chick was found upon the hay,
Its little life had ebbed away,
    No longer frolicsome and gay,
    No longer could it run and play.
"And must we, chicken, must we part?"
Its master § cried with bursting heart,
    And voice of agony and pain.

* The hen's house.
† Beak and claw.   ‡ Press out.
§ Probably one of the two stalwart youths.

27

So one whose ticket's marked "Return," *
When to the lonely roadside station
He flies in fear and perturbation,
Thinks of his home—the hissing urn—
Then runs with flying hat and hair,
And, entering, finds to his despair
He's missed the very latest train.†

Too long it were to tell of each conjecture,
Of chicken suicide and poultry victim,
The deadly frown, the stern and dreary lecture,
The timid guess, "perhaps some needle's pricked him,"
The din of voice, the words both loud and many,
The sob, the tear, the sigh that none could smother,
Till all agreed, "a shilling to a penny
It killed itself, and we acquit the mother!"
Scarce was the verdict spoken,
When that still calm was broken,
A childish form hath burst into the throng,
With tears and looks of sadness,
That bring no news of gladness;
But tell too surely something hath gone wrong!
"The sight that I have come upon
The stoutest heart ‡ would sicken,
That nasty hen has been and gone
And killed another chicken!"

* The system of return tickets is an excellent one. People are conveyed on particular days there and back for one fare.

† An additional vexation would be that his "Return" ticket would be no use the next day.

‡ Perhaps even the bursting heart of its master.

MY FANCY

(From "College Rhymes"*)

I painted her a gushing thing,
  With years perhaps a score;
I little thought to find they were
  At least a dozen more;
My fancy gave her eyes of blue,
  A curly auburn head:
I came to find the blue a green,
  The auburn turned to red.

* This was a Christ Church journal edited by Lewis Carroll during his
Varsity days. "A Sea Dirge" (see next poem) first appeared in it.

Further Nonsense

She boxed my ears this morning,
   They tingled very much;
I own that I could wish her
A somewhat lighter touch;
And if you ask me how
   Her charms might be improved,
I would not have them *added to,*
   But just a few *removed!*

She has the bear's ethereal grace,
   The bland hyena's laugh,
The footstep of the elephant,
   The neck of the giraffe;
I love her still, believe me,
   Though my heart its passion hides;
"She's all my fancy painted her,"
   But oh! *how much besides!*

A SEA DIRGE*

There are certain things—as a spider, a ghost,
   The income-tax, gout, an umbrella for three—
That I hate, but the thing that I hate the most
   Is a thing they call the Sea.

Pour some salt water over the floor—
   Ugly I'm sure you'll allow it to be:
Suppose it extended a mile or more,
   That's very like the Sea.

Beat a dog till it howls outright—
   Cruel, but all very well for a spree:
Suppose that he did so day and night,
   That would be like the Sea.

I had a vision of nursery-maids;
   Tens of thousands passed by me—
All leading children with wooden spades,
   And this was by the Sea.

*One is impelled to suspect that the satire in these verses is intended wholly for effect, and was not at all representative of the author's feelings. Most of his summer holidays were spent by the sea, and his letters contain complimentary references to Whitby, Sandown, Margate, Eastbourne, and other seaside resorts. His particular favourite was Eastbourne, where he seems to have spent most of his summer vacations during the last thirty years of his life.

31

Who invented those spades of wood?
    Who was it cut them out of the tree?
None, I think, but an idiot could—
    Or one that loved the Sea.

It is pleasant and dreamy, no doubt, to float
    With "thoughts as boundless, and souls as free";
But suppose you are very unwell in the boat,*
    How do you like the Sea?

There is an insect that people avoid
    (Whence is derived the verb "to flee"),
Where have you been by it most annoyed?
    In lodgings by the Sea.

If you like coffee with sand for dregs,
    A decided hint of salt in your tea,
And a fishy taste in the very eggs—
    By all means choose the Sea.

And if, with these dainties to drink and eat,
    You prefer not a vestige of grass or tree,
And a chronic state of wet in your feet,
    Then—I recommend the Sea.

For *I* have friends who dwell by the coast—
    Pleasant friends they are to me!
It is when I am with them I wonder most
    That any one likes the Sea.

* Mr. Dodgson himself was an exceptionally good sailor. In his diary for July 13, 1867, describing a Channel crossing, he says: "The pen refuses to describe the sufferings of some of the passengers . . . my own sensations were those of extreme surprise, and a little indignation, at there being no other sensations; it was not for *that* I paid my money."

A Sea Dirge

They take me a walk: though tired and stiff,
   To climb the heights I madly agree:
And, after a tumble or so from the cliff,
   They kindly suggest the Sea.

I try the rocks, and I think it cool
   That they laugh with such an excess of glee,
As I heavily slip into every pool
   That skirts the cold, cold Sea.

LIMERICK *

There was a young lady of station,
   "I love man" was her sole exclamation;
   But when men cried, "You flatter,"
   She replied, "Oh! no matter,
Isle of Man is the true explanation."

* The editor has received this Limerick from Miss Vera Beringer; it is probably the only one Lewis Carroll ever perpetrated. In common with the rest of the English theatre-going public, he was charmed with Miss Beringer's acting as "Little Lord Fauntleroy" in the original London presentation of that play in 1890, and the little girl, as she then was, became one of his many child friends. He sent her the Limerick when she was spending a holiday in Manxland.

34

A BACCHANALIAN ODE *

Here's to the Freshman of bashful eighteen!
　　Here's to the Senior of twenty!
Here's to the youth whose moustache can't be seen!
　　And here's to the man who has plenty!
　　　　Let the men Pass!
　　　　Out of the mass
I'll warrant we'll find you some fit for a Class!

Here's to the Censors, who symbolise Sense,
　　Just as Mitres incorporate Might, Sir!
To the Bursar, who never expands the expense,
　　And the Readers who always do right, Sir.
　　　　Tutor and Don,
　　　　Let them jog on!
I warrant they'll rival the centuries gone!

* From "The Vision of the Three T's" (Oxford, 1873).

A LESSON IN LATIN

(From "The Jabberwock," * June, 1888)

Our Latin books, in motley row,
   Invite us to the task—
Gay Horace, stately Cicero;
Yet there's one verb, when once we know,
   No higher skill we ask:
This ranks all other lore above—
We've learned "amare" means "to love"!

So hour by hour, from flower to flower,
   We sip the sweets of life:
Till ah! too soon the clouds arise,
And knitted brows and angry eyes
   Proclaim the dawn of strife.
With half a smile and half a sigh,
   "Amare!   Bitter One!" we cry.

---

* The magazine of the Girls' Latin School, Boston, Mass. When asked
for permission to use this title, the creator of the Jabberwock characteris-
tically replied:

"Mr. Lewis Carroll has much pleasure in giving to the editors of the
proposed magazine permission to use the title they wish for. He finds that
the Anglo-Saxon word 'wocer' or 'wocor' signifies 'offspring' or 'fruit.'
Taking 'jabber' in its ordinary acceptation of 'excited and voluble discussion,'
this would give the meaning of 'the result of much excited discussion.'
Whether this phrase will have any application to the projected periodical,
it will be for the future historian of American literature to determine.
Mr. Carroll wishes all success to the forthcoming magazine."

A Lesson in Latin

Last night we owned, with looks forlorn,
  "Too well the scholar knows
There is no rose without a thorn"—
But peace is made! we sing this morn,
  "No thorn without a rose!"
Our Latin lesson is complete:
We've learned that Love is "Bitter-sweet"!

THE TWO BROTHERS

(From "The Rectory Umbrella," 1853)

There were two brothers at Twyford school,
  And when they had left the place,
It was, "Will ye learn Greek and Latin?
  Or will ye run me a race?
Or will ye go up to yonder bridge,
  And there we will angle for dace?"

"I'm too stupid for Greek and for Latin,
  I'm too lazy by half for a race,
So I'll go up to yonder bridge,
  And there we will angle for dace."

He has fitted together two joints of his rod,
  And to them he has added another,
And then a great hook he took from his book,
  And ran it right into his brother.

Oh much is the noise that is made among boys
  When playfully pelting a pig,
But a far greater pother was made by his brother
  When flung from the top of the brigg.

The fish hurried up by the dozens,
  All ready and eager to bite,
For the lad that he flung was so tender and young,
  It quite gave them an appetite.

Said, "Thus shall he wallop about
   And the fish take him quite at their ease,
For me to annoy it was ever his joy,
   Now I'll teach him the meaning of 'Tees'!"

The wind to his ear brought a voice,
   "My brother, you didn't had ought ter!
And what have I done that you think it such fun
   To indulge in the pleasure of slaughter?

39

"A good nibble or bite is my chiefest delight,
    When I'm merely expected to *see*,
But a bite from a fish is not quite what I wish,
    When I get it performed upon *me*;
And just now here's a swarm of dace at my arm,
    And a perch has got hold of my knee.

"For water my thirst was not great at the first,
    And of fish I have quite sufficien———"
"Oh fear not!" he cried, "for whatever betide,
    We are both in the selfsame condition!

"I'm sure that our state's very nearly alike
    (Not considering the question of slaughter),
For I have my perch on the top of the bridge,
    And you have your perch in the water.

"I stick to my perch and your perch sticks to you,
    We are really extremely alike!
I've a turn-pike up here, and I very much fear
    You may soon have a turn with a pike."

"Oh grant but one wish!   If I'm took by a fish
    (For your bait is your brother, good man!),
Pull him up if you like, but I hope you will strike
    As gently as ever you can."

"If the fish be a trout, I'm afraid there's no doubt
    I must strike him like lightning that's greased;
If the fish be a pike, I'll engage not to strike,
    Till I've waited ten minutes at least."

40

"But in those ten minutes to desolate Fate
  Your brother a victim may fall!"
"I'll reduce it to five, so *perhaps* you'll survive,
  But the chance is exceedingly small."

"Oh hard is your heart for to act such a part;
  Is it iron, or granite, or steel?"
"Why, I really can't say—it is many a day
  Since my heart was accustomed to feel.

" 'Twas my heart-cherished wish for to slay many fish,
  Each day did my malice grow worse,
For my heart didn't soften with doing it so often,
  But rather, I should say, the reverse."

"Oh would I were back at Twyford school,
  Learning lessons in fear of the birch!"
"Nay, brother!" he cried, "for whatever betide,
  You are better off here with your perch!

"I'm sure you'll allow you are happier now,
  With nothing to do but to play;
And this single line here, it is perfectly clear,
  Is much better than thirty a day!

"And as to the rod hanging over your head,
  And apparently ready to fall,
That, you know, was the case when you lived in that place,
  So it need not be reckoned at all.

"Do you see that old trout with a turn-up nose snout?
  (Just to speak on a pleasanter theme.)
Observe, my dear brother, our love for each other—
  He's the one I like best in the stream.

"To-morrow I mean to invite him to dine
  (We shall all of us think it a treat),
If the day should be fine, I'll just *drop him a line*,
  And we'll settle what time we're to meet.

"He hasn't been into society yet,
  And his manners are not of the best,
So I think it quite fair that it should be *my care*,
  To see that he's properly dressed.

"I know there are people who prate by the hour
  Of the beauty of earth, sky, and ocean;
Of the birds as they fly, of the fish darting by,
  Rejoicing in Life and in Motion.

"As to any delight to be got from the sight,
  It is all very well for a flat,
But *I* think it gammon, for hooking a salmon
  Is better than twenty of that!

"They say that a man of right-thinking mind
  Will *love* the dumb creatures he sees—
What's the use of his mind, if he's never inclined
  To pull a fish out of the Tees?

"Take my friends and my home—as an outcast I'll roam:
  Take the money I have in the Bank:
It is just what I wish, but deprive me of *fish*,
  And my life would indeed be a blank!"
    *   *   *   *   *
Forth from the house his sister came,
  Her brothers for to see,
But when she saw the sight of awe,
  The tear stood in her e'e.

The Two Brothers

"Oh what's that bait upon your hook,
  My brother, tell to me?"
"It is but the fan-tailed pigeon,
  He would not sing for me."

"Whoe'er would expect a pigeon to sing,
  A simpleton he must be!
But a pigeon-cote is a different thing
  To the coat that there I see!

"Oh what's that bait upon your hook,
  Dear brother, tell to me?"
"It is my younger brother," he cried,
  Oh woe and dole is me!

"I's mighty wicked, that I is!
  Oh how could such things be?
Farewell, farewell, sweet sister,
  I'm going o'er the sea."

"And when will you come back again,
  My brother, tell to me?"
"When chub is good for human food,
  And that will never be!"

She turned herself right round about,
  And her heart brake into three,
Said, "One of the two will be wet through and through,
  And t'other'll be late for his tea!"

43

POETRY FOR THE MILLION

(From "The Rectory Umbrella")

The nineteenth century has produced a new school of music, bearing about the same relation to the genuine article which the hash or stew of Monday does to the joint of Sunday.*

We allude, of course, to the prevalent practice of diluting the works of earlier composers with washy modern variations, so as to suit the weakened and depraved taste of this generation; this invention is termed "setting" by some, who, scorning the handsome offer of Alexander Smith to "set this age to music," have determined to set music to this age.

Sadly we admit the stern necessity that exists for such a change; with stern prophetic eye we see looming in the shadowy Future the downfall of the sister Fine Arts. The National Gallery have already subjected some of their finest pictures to this painful operation. Poetry must follow.

That we may not be behind others in forwarding the progress of Civilisation, we boldly discard all personal and private feelings, and with quivering pen and tear-dimmed eye we dedicate the following composition to the Spirit of the Age, and to that noble band of gallant adventurers who aspire to lead the van in the great march of reform.

*What *would* Mr. Carroll have said with regard to the epileptic style in musical composition which is in vogue in this present year of grace? Possibly he would have been "inspired" to write a companion poem to "Jabberwocky," with the Demon of Jazz as its "manxome foe."

RHYMED CORRESPONDENCE *

DEAR MAGGIE.—I found that the *friend*, that the little girl asked me to write to, lived at Ripon, and not at Land's End—a nice sort of place to invite to! It looked rather suspicious to me—and soon after, by dint of incessant inquiries, I found out that *she* was called Maggie, and lived in a Crescent! Of course I declared,

"After that" (the language I used doesn't matter), "I will *not* address her, that's flat! So do not expect me to flatter."

*From a letter written to Miss Maggie Cunningham in 1868. The fairy-tale referred to was "Bruno's Revenge," which, more than twenty years later, Lewis Carroll developed into "Sylvie and Bruno."

No *carte* has yet been done of me, that does real justice to my *smile;* and so I hardly like, you see, to send you one. However, I'll consider if I will or not—meanwhile, I send a little thing to give

you an idea of what I look like when I'm lecturing. The merest sketch, you will allow—yet still I think there's something grand in the expression of the brow and in the action of the hand.

Have you read my fairy-tale in "Aunt Judy's Magazine"? If you have you will not fail to discover what I mean when I say, "Bruno yesterday came to remind me that *he* was my godson!"— on the ground that I "gave him a name"!

ACROSTICS

Second only to Lewis Carroll's stories in the delight they afforded his young friends were his acrostics, in the composition of which he showed a remarkable talent. There were few of his child favourites whose names he did not embody in verses of this kind; some, as in the case of Isa Bowman in "Sylvie and Bruno," and Gertrude Chataway in "The Hunting of the Snark," he recorded for posterity in acrostical dedications in his books, but most of these rhymes were composed merely for the amusement of the children concerned, with no thought of publication.

One of the best he wrote across the fly-leaf of a copy of "The Hunting of the Snark," which he sent to Miss Adelaide Paine in 1876. It runs thus:

"A re you deaf, Father William?" the young man said.
"D id you hear what I told you just now?
"E xcuse me for shouting!   Don't waggle your head
"L ike a blundering, sleepy old cow!
"A little maid dwelling in Wallington Town,
"I s my friend, so I beg to remark:
"D o you think she'd be pleased if a book were sent down
"E ntitled 'The Hunt of the Snark'?"

"P ack it up in brown paper!" the old man cried,
"A nd seal it with olive-and-dove.
"I command you to do it!" he added with pride,
"N or forget, my good fellow, to send her beside
"E aster Greetings, and give her my love."

49

Very few of Mr. Carroll's acrostics were in this nonsensical strain, however, the vast majority being either serious or quaintly complimentary, as in this example on the name of Miss Sarah Sinclair (1878):

LOVE AMONG THE ROSES

S eek ye Love, ye fairy-sprites?
A nd where reddest roses grow,
R osy fancies he invites,
A nd in roses he delights,
H ave ye found him? "No!"

S eek again, and find the boy
I n Childhood's heart, so pure and clear.
N ow the fairies leap for joy,
C rying, "Love is here!"
L ove has found his proper nest;
A nd we guard him while he dozes
I n a dream of peace and rest
R osier than roses.

MAGGIE'S VISIT TO OXFORD *

(June 9th to 13th)

When Maggie once to Oxford came,
    On tour as "Bootles' Baby,"
She said, "I'll see this place of fame,
    However dull the day be."

So with her friend she visited
    The sights that it was rich in:
And first of all she popped her head
    Inside the Christ Church kitchen.

The Cooks around that little child
    Stood waiting in a ring:
And every time that Maggie smiled
    Those Cooks began to sing—
Shouting the Battle-cry of Freedom! †

* These verses, never intended for publication, were written to amuse the child actress, little Maggie Bowman, when she visited Oxford to play the title-rôle in the stage version of John Strange Winter's popular novel, "Bootles' Baby."

† In a letter to the editor, the charming lady to whom these pleasing verses were sent says: "This line is introduced because he told me a story of some soldiers who could never remember the words of their marching song, except for the last line, so they used to sing the words of 'Mary had a little lamb,' finishing with 'The lamb was sure to go—Shouting the Battle-cry of Freedom'!"

"Roast, boil and bake,
For Maggie's sake:
Bring cutlets fine
For *her* to dine,
Meringues so sweet
For her to eat—
For Maggie may be
Bootles' Baby!"

Then hand in hand in pleasant talk
  They wandered and admired
The Hall, Cathedral and Broad Walk,
  Till Maggie's feet were tired:

To Worcester Garden next they strolled,
  Admired its quiet lake:
Then to St. John, a college old,
  Their devious way they take.

In idle mood they sauntered round
  Its lawn so green and flat,
And in that garden Maggie found
  A lovely Pussy-Cat!

A quarter of an hour they spent
  In wandering to and fro:
  And everywhere that Maggie went,
  The Cat was sure to go—
Shouting the Battle-cry of Freedom!

"Maiow! Maiow!
Come, make your bow,
Take off your hats,
Ye Pussy-Cats!

52

And purr and purr,
To welcome *her*,
For Maggie may be
Bootles' Baby!"

So back to Christ Church, not too late
    For them to go and see
A Christ Church undergraduate,*
    Who gave them cake and tea.

Next day she entered with her guide
    The garden called "Botanic,"
And there a fierce Wild Boar she spied,
    Enough to cause a panic:

But Maggie didn't mind, not she,
    She would have faced, alone,
That fierce wild boar, because, you see,
    The thing was made of stone.

On Magdalen walls they saw a face
    That filled her with delight,
A giant face, that made grimace
    And grinned with all its might.

A little friend, industrious,
    Pulled upwards all the while
The corner of its mouth, and thus
    He helped that face to smile!

* A nephew of Lewis Carroll.

"How nice," thought Maggie, "it would be
    If *I* could have a friend
To do that very thing for *me*
And make my mouth turn up with glee,
    By pulling at one end."

In Magdalen Park the deer are wild
    With joy, that Maggie brings
Some bread a friend had given the child,
    To feed the pretty things.

They flock round Maggie without fear:
    They breakfast and they lunch,
They dine, they sup, those happy deer—
    Still, as they munch and munch
Shouting the Battle-cry of Freedom!

    "Yes, Deer are we,
    And dear is she!
    We love this child
    So sweet and mild:
    We all rejoice
    At Maggie's voice:
    We all are fed
    With Maggie's bread . . .
    For Maggie may be
    Bootles' Baby!"

They met a Bishop * on their way . . .
    A Bishop large as life,
With loving smile that seemed to say
    "Will Maggie be my wife?"

    * The then Bishop of Oxford.

Maggie's Visit to Oxford

Maggie thought *not*, because, you see,
  She was so *very* young,
And he was old as old could be . . .
  So Maggie held her tongue.

"My Lord, she's Bootles' Baby, we
  Are going up and down,"
Her friend explained, "that she may see
  The sights of Oxford Town."

"Now say what kind of place it is,"
  The Bishop gaily cried.
"The best place in the Provinces!"
  That little maid replied.

Away, next morning, Maggie went
  From Oxford town: but yet
The happy hours she had there spent
  She could not soon forget.

The train is gone, it rumbles on:
  The engine-whistle screams;
But Maggie deep in rosy sleep . . .
  And softly in her dreams,
Whispers the Battle-cry of Freedom.

      "Oxford, good-bye!"
      She seems to sigh.
      "You dear old City,
      With gardens pretty,
      And lanes and flowers,

And college-towers,
And Tom's great Bell . . .
Farewell—farewell:
For Maggie may be
Bootles' Baby!"

WILHELM VON SCHMITZ *
(From "The Whitby Gazette," September 7, 1854)

CHAPTER ONE

" 'Twas ever thus."
(Old Play.)

The sultry glare of noon was already giving place to the cool of a cloudless evening, and the lulled ocean was washing against the Pier with a low murmur, suggestive to poetical minds of the kindred ideas of motion and lotion, when two travellers might have been seen, by such as chose to look that way, approaching the secluded town of Whitby by one of those headlong paths, dignified by the name of road, which serve as entrances into the place, and which were originally constructed, it is supposed, on the somewhat fantastic model of pipes running into a water-butt. The elder of the two was a sallow and careworn man; his features were adorned with what had been often at a distance mistaken for a moustache, and were shaded by a beaver hat, of doubtful age, and of appearance which, if not respectable, was at least venerable. The younger, in whom the sagacious reader already recognises the hero of my tale, possessed a form which, once seen, could scarcely be forgotten: a slight tendency to obesity proved but a trifling drawback to the manly grace of its contour, and though the strict laws of beauty might perhaps have required a somewhat longer pair of legs to make up the proportion of his figure, and that his eyes should match rather more exactly than they chanced to do, yet to those critics who

* See footnote to "The Lady of the Ladle."

are untrammelled with any laws of taste, and there are many such, to those who could close their eyes to the faults in his shape, and single out its beauties, though few were ever found capable of the task, to those above all who knew and esteemed his personal character, and believed that the powers of his mind transcended those of the age he lived in, though alas! none such has as yet turned up —to those he was a very Apollo.

What though it had not been wholly false to assert that too much grease had been applied to his hair, and too little soap to his hands? that his nose turned too much up, and his shirt collars too much down? that his whiskers had borrowed all the colour from his cheeks, excepting a little that had run down into his waistcoat? Such trivial criticisms were unworthy the notice of any who laid claim to the envied title of the connoisseur.

He had been christened William, and his father's name was Smith, but though he had introduced himself to many of the higher circles in London under the imposing name of "Mr. Smith, of Yorkshire," he had unfortunately not attracted so large a share of public notice as he was confident he merited: some had asked him how far back he traced his ancestry; others had been mean enough to hint that his position in society was not entirely unique; while the sarcastic enquiries of others touching the dormant peerage in his family, to which, it was suggested, he was about to lay claim, had awakened in the breast of the noble-spirited youth an ardent longing for that high birth and connection which an adverse Fortune had denied him.

Hence he had conceived the notion of that fiction, which perhaps in his case must be considered merely as a poetical licence, whereby he passed himself off upon the world under the sounding appellation which heads this tale. This step had already occasioned a large increase in his popularity, a circumstance which his friends spoke of under the unpoetical simile of a bad sovereign fresh gilt, but which he himself more pleasantly described as, " . . . a violet pale, At length discovered in its mossy dale, And borne to sit with kings": a destiny for which, as it is generally believed, violets are not naturally fitted.

The travellers, each buried in his own thoughts, paced in silence down the steep, save when an unusually sharp stone, or an unexpected dip in the road, produced one of those involuntary exclamations of pain, which so triumphantly demonstrate the connection between Mind and Matter. At length the young traveller, rousing himself with an effort from his painful reverie, broke upon the meditations of his companion with the unexpected question, "Think you she will be much altered in feature? I trust me not." "Think who?" testily rejoined the other: then hastily correcting himself, with an exquisite sense of grammar, he substituted the expressive phrase. "Who's the she you're after?" "Forget you then," asked the young man, who was so intensely poetical in soul that he never spoke in ordinary prose, "forget you the subject we conversed on but now? Trust me, she hath dwelt in my thoughts ever since." "But now!" his friend repeated, in sarcastic tone, "it is an hour good since you spoke last." The young man nodded assent; "An hour? true, true. We were passing Lyth, as I bethink me, and lowly in thine ear was I murmuring that touching sonnet to the sea I writ of late, beginning, 'Thou roaring, snoring, heaving, grieving main which——'" "For pity's sake!" interrupted the other, and there was real earnestness in that pleading tone, "don't let us have it all again! I have heard it with patience once already."

"Thou hast, thou hast," the baffled poet replied: "well then, she shall again be the topic of my thoughts," and he frowned and bit his lip, muttering to himself such words as cooky, hooky, and crooky, as if he were trying to find a rhyme to something. And now the pair were passing near a bridge, and shops were on their left and water on their right; and from beneath uprose a confused hubbub

59

of sailors' voices, and, wafted on the landward breeze, came an aroma, dimly suggestive of salt herring, and all things from the heaving waters in the harbour to the light smoke that floated gracefully above the housetops, suggested nought but poetry to the mind of the gifted youth.

CHAPTER TWO

"And I, for one."
(*Old Play.*)

"But about she," resumed the man of prose, "what's her name? You never told me that yet." A faint flush crossed the interesting features of the youth; could it be that her name was unpoetical, and did not consort with his ideas of the harmony of nature? He spoke reluctantly and indistinctly; "Her name," he faintly gasped, "is Sukie."

A long, low whistle was the only reply; thrusting his hands deep in his pockets, the elder speaker turned away, while the unhappy youth, whose delicate nerves were cruelly shaken by his friend's ridicule, grasped the railing near to him to steady his tottering feet. Distant sounds of melody from the Cliff at this moment reached their ears, and while his unfeeling comrade wandered in the direction of the Music, the distressed poet hastily sought the Bridge, to give his pent-up feelings vent, unnoticed by the passers-by.

The Sun was setting as he reached the spot, and the still surface of the waters below, as he crossed on to the Bridge, calmed his perturbed spirit, and sadly leaning his elbows on the rail, he pondered. What visions filled that noble soul, as, with features that would have beamed with intelligence, had they only possessed an expression at all, and a frown that only needed dignity to be appalling, he fixed upon the sluggish tide those fine though bloodshot eyes?

Visions of his early days; scenes from the happy time of pinafores, treacle, and innocence; through the long vista of the past came floating spectres of long-forgotten spelling-books, slates scrawled thick with dreary sums, that seldom came out at all, and never came out right; tingling and somewhat painful sensations returned to his knuckles and the roots of his hair; he was a boy once more.

"Now, young man there!" so broke a voice upon the air, "tak whether o' the two roads thou likes, but thou can't stop in't middle!" The words fell idly on his ears, or served but to suggest new trains of reverie; "Roads, aye, roads," he whispered low, and then louder, as the glorious idea burst upon him, "Aye, and am I not the Colossus of Rhodes?" he raised his manly form erect at the thought, and planted his feet with a firmer stride.

. . . Was it but a delusion of his heated brain? or stern reality? slowly, slowly yawned the bridge beneath him, and now his footing is already grown unsteady, and now the dignity of his attitude is gone: he recks not, come what may; is he not a Colossus?

. . . The stride of a Colossus is possibly equal to any emergency; the elasticity of fustian is limited: it was at this critical juncture that "the force of nature could no further go," and therefore deserted him, while the force of gravity began to operate in its stead.

In other words, he fell.

And the "Hilda" went slowly on its way, and knew not that it passed a poet under the Bridge, and guessed not whose were those two feet, that disappeared through the eddying waters, kicking with spasmodic energy; and men pulled into a boat a dripping, panting form, that resembled a drowned rat rather than a Poet; and spoke to it without awe, and even said, "young feller," and something about "greenhorn," and laughed; what knew they of Poetry?

Turn we to other scenes: a long, low room, with high-backed settees, and a sanded floor: a knot of men drinking and gossiping: a general prevalence of tobacco; a powerful conviction that spirits existed somewhere: and she, the fair Sukie herself, gliding airily through the scene, and bearing in those lily hands—what? Some garland doubtless, wreathed of the most fragrant flowers that grow? Some cherished volume, morocco-bound and golden-clasped, the works immortal of the bard of eld, whereon she loveth oft to ponder? Possibly, "The Poems of William Smith," that idol of her affections, in two volumes quarto, published some years agone, whereof one copy only has as yet been sold, and that he bought himself—to give to Sukie. Which of these is it that the beauteous maiden carries with such tender care? Alas none: it is but those two "goes of arf-and-arf, warm without," which have just been ordered by the guests in the tap-room.

In a small parlour hard by, unknown, untended, though his Sukie was so near, wet, moody, and dishevelled, sat the youth: the fire had been kindled at his desire, and before it he was now drying himself, but as "the cheery blaze, Blithe harbinger of wintry days," to use his own powerful description, consisted at present of a feeble, spluttering faggot, whose only effect was to half-choke him with its smoke, he may be pardoned for not feeling, more keenly than he does, that " . . . fire of Soul, When gazing on the kindling coal, A Britain feels that, spite of fone, He wots his native hearth his own!" we again employ his own thrilling words on the subject.

The waiter, unconscious that a Poet sat before him, was talking confidingly; he dwelt on various themes, and still the youth sat heedless, but when at last he spoke of Sukie, those dull eyes flashed with fire, and cast upon the speaker a wild glance of scornful defiance, that was unfortunately wasted, as its object was stirring the fire at the moment and failed to notice it. "Say, oh say those words again!" he gasped. "I surely heard thee not aright!" The waiter looked astonished, but obligingly repeated his remark, "I were merely a saying, sir, that she's an uncommon clever girl, and as how I were 'oping some day to hacquire her Hart, if so be that——" He said no more, for the Poet. with a groan of anguish, had rushed distractedly from the room.

CHAPTER THREE

"Nay, 'tis too much!"
(*Old Play.*)

Night, solemn night.

On the present occasion the solemnity of night's approach was rendered far more striking than it is to dwellers in ordinary towns, by that time-honoured custom observed by the people of Whitby, of leaving their streets wholly unlighted: in thus making a stand against the deplorably swift advance of the tide of progress and civilisation, they displayed no small share of moral courage and independent judgement. Was it for a people of sense to adopt every new-fangled invention of the age, merely because their neighbours did? It might have been urged, in disparagement of their conduct, that they only injured themselves by it, and the remark would have been undeniably true; but it would only have served to exalt, in the eyes of an admiring nation, their well-earned character of heroic self-denial and uncompromising fixity of purpose.

Headlong and desperate, the lovelorn Poet plunged through the night; now tumbling up against a doorstep, and now half down in a gutter, but ever onward, onward, reckless where he went.

In the darkest spot of one of those dark streets (the nearest lighted shop window being about fifty yards off), chance threw into his way the very man he fled from, the man whom he hated as a successful rival, and who had driven him to this pitch of frenzy. The waiter, not knowing what was the matter, had followed him to see that he came to no harm, and to bring him back, little dreaming of the shock that awaited him.

The instant the Poet perceived who it was, all his pent-up fury broke forth: to rush upon him, to grasp him by the throat with both hands, to dash him to the ground, and there to reduce him to the extreme verge of suffocation—all this was the work of a moment.

"Traitor! villain! malcontent! regicide!" he hissed through his closed teeth, taking any abusive epithet that came into his head, without stopping to consider its suitability. "Is it thou? Now shalt thou feel my wrath!" And doubtless the waiter did experience that singular sensation, whatever it may have been, for he struggled violently with his assailant, and bellowed "murder" the instant he recovered his breath.

"Say not so," the Poet sternly answered, as he released him; "it is thou that murderest me." The waiter gathered himself up, and began in great surprise, "Why, I never——" "'Tis a lie!" the Poet screamed; "she loves thee not! Me, me alone." "Who ever said she did?" the other asked, beginning to perceive how matters stood. "Thou! thou saidst it," was the wild reply, "what, villain? acquire her heart? thou never shalt."

The waiter calmly explained himself: "My 'ope were, Sir, to hacquire her Hart of waiting at table, which she do perdigious well, sure-ly: seeing that I were thinking of happlying for to be 'ead-waiter at the 'otel." The Poet's wrath instantly abated, indeed, he looked rather crestfallen than otherwise; "Excuse my violence," he gently said, "and let us take a friendly glass together." "I agree," was the waiter's generous answer, "but man halive, you've ruinated my coat!"

"Courage," cried our hero gaily, "thou shalt have a new one anon: aye, and of the best cashmere." "H'm," said the other, hesitatingly, "wouldn't hany other stuff——" "I will not buy thee one of any other stuff," returned the Poet, gently but decidedly, and the waiter gave up the point.

Arrived once more at the friendly tavern, the Poet briskly ordered a jorum of Punch, and, on its being furnished, called on his friend for a toast. "I'll give you," said the waiter, who was of a sentimental turn, however little he looked like it, "I'll give you— Woman! She doubles our sorrows and 'alves our joy." The Poet drained his glass, not caring to correct his companion's mistake, and at intervals during the evening the same inspiring sentiment was repeated. And so the night wore away, and another jorum of Punch was ordered, and another.

* * * * *

"And now hallow me," said the waiter, attempting for about the tenth time to rise on his feet and make a speech, and failing even more signally than he had yet done, "to give a toast for this 'appy hoccasion. Woman! she doubles——" but at this moment, probably in illustration of his favourite theory, he "doubled" himself up, and so effectually, that he instantly vanished under the table.

Occupying that limited sphere of observation, it is conjectured that he fell to moralising on human ills in general, and their remedies, for a solemn voice was presently heard to issue from his retreat, proclaiming feelingly though rather indistinctly, that "when the 'art of man is hopressed with care——," here came a pause, as if he wished to leave the question open to discussion, but as no one present seemed competent to suggest the proper course to be taken in that melancholy contingency, he attempted to supply the deficiency himself with the remarkable statement "she's hall my fancy painted 'er."

Meanwhile the Poet was sitting, smiling quietly to himself, as he sipped his punch: the only notice he took of his companion's abrupt disappearance was to help himself to a fresh glass, and say, "your health!" in a cordial tone, nodding to where the waiter ought to have been. He then cried, "hear, hear!" encouragingly, and made an attempt to thump the table with his fist, but missed it. He seemed interested in the question regarding the heart oppressed with care, and winked sagaciously with one eye two or three times, as if there were a good deal he could say on that subject, if he chose; but the second quotation roused him to speech, and he at once broke into the waiter's subterranean soliloquy with an ecstatic fragment from the poem he had been just composing:

"What though the world be cross and crooky?
Of Life's fair flowers the fairest bouquet
I plucked, when I chose *thee*, my Sukie!

"Say, could'st thou grasp at nothing greater
Than to be wedded to a waiter?
And did'st thou deem thy Schmitz a traitor?

"Nay! the fond waiter was rejected,
And thou, alone, with flower-bedecked head,
Sitting, did'st sing of one expected.

"And while the waiter, crazed and silly,
Dreamed he had won that precious lily,
At length he came, thy wished-for Willie.

"And then thy music took a new key,
For whether Schmitz be boor or duke, he
Is all in all to faithful Sukie!"

He paused for a reply, but a heavy snoring from beneath the table was the only one he got.

CHAPTER FOUR

"Is this the hend?"
("*Nicholas Nickleby.*")

Bathed in the radiance of the newly-risen Sun, the billows are surging and bristling below the Cliff, along which the Poet is thoughtfully wending his way. It may possibly surprise the reader that he should not ere this have obtained an interview with his beloved Sukie: he may ask the reason: he will ask in vain: to record with rigid accuracy the progress of events is the sole duty of the historian: were he to go beyond that, and attempt to dive into the hidden causes of things, the why and the wherefore, he would be trespassing on the province of the metaphysician.

Presently the Poet reached a small rising ground at the end of the gravel walk, where he found a seat commanding a view of the sea, and here he sunk down wearily.

For a while he gazed dreamily upon the expanse of ocean, then, struck by a sudden thought, he opened a small pocket book, and proceeded to correct and complete his last poem. Slowly to himself he muttered the words "death—saith—breath," impatiently tapping the ground with his foot. "Ah, that'll do," he said at last, with an air of relief, "breath":

> "His barque had perished in the storm,
>   Whirled by its fiery breath
> On sunken rocks, his stalwart form
>   Was doomed to watery death."

"That last line's good," he continued exaltingly, "and on Coleridge's principle of alliteration, too—W. D., W. D.—was doomed to watery death."

"Take care," growled a deep voice in his ear, "what you say will be used in evidence against you—now it's no use trying that, we've got you tight," this last remark being caused by the struggles of the Poet, naturally indignant at being unexpectedly collared by two men from behind.

"He's confessed to it, constable? you heard him?" said the first speaker (who rejoiced in the euphonious title of Muggle, and whom it is almost superfluous to introduce to the reader as the elder traveller of Chapter One)! "it's as much as his life is worth."

"I say, stow that——" warmly responded the other; "seems to me the gen'leman was a spouting potry."

"What—what's the matter?" here gasped our unfortunate hero, who had recovered his breath; "you—Muggle—what do you mean by it?"

"Mean by it!" blustered his quondam friend, "what do *you* mean by it, if you comes to that? You're an assassin, that's what you are! Where's the waiter you had with you last night? answer me that!"

"The—the waiter?" slowly repeated the Poet, still stunned by the suddenness of his capture, "why, he's dr——"

"I knew it!" cried his friend, who was at him in a moment, and choked up the unfinished word in his throat, "drowned, Constable! I told you so—and who did it?" he continued, loosing his grip a moment to obtain an answer.

The Poet's answer, so far as it could be gathered, (for it came out in a very fragmentary state, and as it were by crumbs, in intervals of choking) was the following: "It was my—my—you'll kill me—fault—I say, fault—I—I—gave him—you—you're suffoca —I say—I gave him——" "a push I suppose," concluded the other, who here "shut off" the slender supply of breath he had hitherto allowed his victim "and he fell in: no doubt. I heard some one had fallen off the Bridge last night," turning to the Constable; "no doubt this unfortunate waiter. Now mark my words! from this

68

moment I renounce this man as my friend: don't pity him, constable! don't think of letting him go to spare *my* feelings!"

Some convulsive sounds were heard at this moment from the Poet, which, on attentive consideration, were found to be "the punch —was—was too much—for him—quite—it—quite——" "Miserable man!" sternly interposed Muggle; "can you jest about it? You gave him a punch, did you? and what then?"

"It quite—quite—upset him," continued the unhappy Schmitz, in a sort of rambling soliloquy, which was here cut short by the impatience of the Constable, and the party set forth on their return to the town.

But an unexpected character burst upon the scene and broke into a speech far more remarkable for energetic delivery than for grammatical accuracy: "I've only just 'erd of it—I were hasleep under table—'avin' taken more punch than I could stand—he's as hinnocent as I am—dead indeed! I'm more alive than you, a precious sight!"

This speech produced various effects on its hearers: the Constable calmly released his man, the bewildered Muggle muttered "Impossible! conspiracy—perjury—have it tried at assizes": while the happy Poet rushed into the arms of his deliverer crying in a broken voice: "No, never from this hour to part. We'll live and love so true!" a sentiment which the waiter did not echo with the cordiality that might have been expected.

Later in the day, Wilhelm and Sukie were sitting conversing with the waiter and a few friends, when the penitent Muggle suddenly entered the room, placed a folded paper on the knees of Schmitz, pronounced in a hollow tone the affecting words "be happy!" vanished, and was seen no more.

After perusing the paper, Wilhelm rose to his feet; in the excitement of the moment he was roused into unconscious and extempore verse:

Further Nonsense

"My Sukie! He hath bought, yea, Muggle's self,
Convinced at last of deeds unjust and foul,
The licence of a vacant public-house.
We are licensed here to sell to all,
Spirits, porter, snuff, and ale!"

So we leave him: his after happiness who dare to doubt? has he
not Sukie? and having her, he is content.

B. B.

THE THREE CATS *

A very curious thing happened to me at half-past four, yesterday. Three visitors came knocking at my door, begging me to let them in. And when I opened the door, who do you think they were?

You'll never guess.

Why, they were three cats! Wasn't it curious? However, they all looked so cross and disagreeable that I took up the first thing I could lay my hand on (which happened to be the rolling pin) and knocked them all down as flat as pancakes!

"If *you* come knocking at my door," I said, "I shall come knocking at your heads."

That was fair, wasn't it?

Of course I didn't leave them lying flat on the ground, like dried flowers: no, I picked them up, and I was as kind as I could be to them. I lent them the portfolio for a bed—they wouldn't have been comfortable in a real bed, you know: they were too thin—but they were *quite* happy between the sheets of blotting paper—and each of them had a pen-wiper for a pillow. Well, then I went to bed: but first I lent them the three dinner-bells to ring if they wanted anything in the night.

You know I have *three* dinner-bells—the first (which is the larg-

---

* This fascinating little fantasy ran through a series of letters which Lewis Carroll wrote to two little friends of his named Agnes and Amy Hughes. Without altering a word of the original and merely by extracting the extraneous matter, the editor has been able to reproduce the complete story, and to present what is, in effect, a new "wonder-tale" in miniature by the author of "Alice in Wonderland," which, in his opinion, is in his best and most characteristic vein.

est) is rung when dinner is *nearly* ready; the second (which is rather larger) is rung when it is quite ready; and the third (which is as large as the other two put together) is rung all the time I am at

dinner. And I told them they must ring if they happened to want anything. And, as they rung *all* the bells *all* night, I suppose they did want something or other, only I was too sleepy to attend to them.

In the morning I gave them some rat-tail jelly and buttered mice for breakfast and they were as discontented as they could be. And, do you know, when I had gone out for a walk, they got *all* my books out of the bookcase, and opened them on the floor to be ready for me to read. They opened them at page 50, because they thought that would be a nice useful page to begin at. It was rather unfortunate, though: because they took my bottle of gum and tried to gum pictures upon the ceiling (which they thought would please me). They accidentally spilt a quantity of it all over the books. So when they were shut up and put by, the leaves all stuck together, and I can never read page 50 again in any of them!

However, they meant it very kindly, so I wasn't angry. I gave them each a spoonful of ink as a treat; but they were ungrateful for that and made the most dreadful faces. But, of course, as it was given them for a treat, they had to drink it. One of them has turned black since: it was a white cat to begin with.

They wanted some boiled pelican, but, of course, I knew it wouldn't be good for them. So all I said was "Go to Agnes Hughes, and if it's *really* good for you she'll give you some."

Then I shook hands with them all, and wished them good-bye, and drove them up the chimney. They seemed very sorry to go.

THE LEGEND OF SCOTLAND *

Being a true and terrible report touching the rooms of Auckland Castell, called Scotland, and of the things there endured by Matthew Dixon, Chaffer, and of a certain Ladye, called Gaunless of some, there apparent, and how that none durst in these days sleep therein (belike through fear,) all which things fell out in ye days of Bishop Bec, of chearfull memorie, and were writ down by mee in the Yeere One Thousand Three Hundred and Twenty Five, in the Month February, on a certayn Tuesday and other days.

EDGAR CUTHWELLIS.

Now the said Matthew Dixon, having fetched wares unto that place, my Loords commended the same, and bade that hee should be entertained for that night, (which in sooth hee was, supping with a grete Appetite,) and sleep in a certayn roome of that apartment now called Scotland—From whence at Midnight hee rushed forth with so grete a Screem, as awaked all men, and hastily running into those Passages, and meeting him so screeming, hee presentlie faynted away.

Whereon they hadde hym into my Loorde's parlour, and with much ado set hym on a Chaire, wherefrom hee three several times split even to the grounde, to the grete admiration of all men.

* "The Legend of Scotland" was written by Lewis Carroll for the daughters of Archbishop Longley, while the latter, as Bishop of Durham, was living at Auckland Castle, and between the years 1856-1860. The legend was suggested by some markings upon the walls of a cellar in a part of the Castle which, from its remoteness and chilliness, was, and perhaps still is, called "Scotland."

But being stayed with divers Strong Liquors, (and, chifest, wyth Gin,) he after a whyle gave foorth in a lamentable tone these following particulars, all which were presentlie sworn to by nine painful and stout farmers, who lived hard by, which witness I will heare orderlie set downe.

Witness of Matthew Dixon, Chaffer, being in my right minde, and more than Fortie Yeeres of Age, though sore affrighted by reason of Sightes and Sounds in This Castell endured by mee, as touching the Vision of Scotland, and the Ghosts, all two of them, therein contayned, and of A certayn straunge Ladye, and of the lamentable thyngs by her uttered, with other sad tunes and songs, by her and by other Ghosts devised, and of the coldness and shakyng of my Bones (through sore grete feer,) and of other things very pleasant to knowe, cheefly of a Picture hereafter suddenlie to bee taken, and of what shall befall thereon, (as trulie foreshowne by Ghosts,) and of Darkness, with other things more terrible than Woordes, and of that which Men call Chimera.

Matthew Dixon, Chaffer, deposeth: "that hee, having supped well over Night on a Green Goose, a Pasty, and other Condiments of the Bishop's grete bountie provided, (looking, as he spake, at my Loorde, and essaying toe pull offe hys hatte untoe hym, but missed soe doing, for that hee hadde yt not on hys hedde,) soe went untoe hys bedde, where of a long tyme hee was exercysed with sharp and horrible Dreems. That hee saw yn hys Dreem a young Ladye, habited, (not as yt seemed) yn a Gaun, but yn a certayn sorte of Wrapper, perchance a Wrap-Rascal." (Hereon a Mayde of the House affirmed that noe Ladye woold weare such a thing, and hee answered, "I stand corrected," and indeed rose from hys chaire, yet fayled to stand.)

Witness continued: "that ye sayde Ladye waved toe and froe a Grete Torche, whereat a thin Voyce shreeked 'Gaunless! Gaunless!' and Shee standyng yn the midst of the floor, a grete Chaunge befell

75

her, her Countenance waxing ever more and more Aged, and her Hayr grayer, shee all that tyme saying yn a most sad Voyce, 'Gaunless, now, as Ladyes bee: yet yn yeeres toe come they shall not lacke for Gauns.' At whych her Wrapper seemed slowlie toe melte, chaunging into a gaun of sylk, which puckered up and down, yea, and flounced itself out not a lyttle": (at thys mye Loorde, waxing impatient, smote hym roundlie onne the hedde, bydding hym finish hys tale anon.)

Witness continued: "that the sayd Gaun thenne chaunged ytself into divers fashyons whych shall hereafter bee, loopyng ytself uppe yn thys place and yn that, soe gyving toe View ane pettycote of a most fiery hue, even Crimson toe looke upon, at whych dismal and blode-thirstie sight he both groned and wepte. That at the laste the skyrt swelled unto a Vastness beyond Man's power toe tell ayded, (as hee judged,) bye Hoops, Cartwheels, Balloons, and the lyke, bearing yt uppe within. That yt fylled alle that Chamber, crushing hym flat untoe hys beddc, tylle such as she appeared toe depart, fryzzling hys Hayre with her Torche as she went.

"That hee, awakyng from such Dreems, herd thereon a Rush, and saw a Light." (Hereon a Mayde interrupted hym, crying out that there was yndeed a Rush-Light burning yn that same room, and woulde have sayde more, but that my Loorde checkt her, and sharplie bade her stow that, meening thereby, that she shoulde holde her peece.)

Witness continued: "that being muche affrited thereat, whereby hys Bones were, (as hee sayde,) all of a dramble, hee essayed to leep from hys bedde, and soe quit. Yet tarried hee some whyle, not, as might bee thought from being stout of Harte, but rather of Bodye; whych tyme she caunted snatches of old lays, as Maister Wil Shakespeare hath yt."

Hereon my Loorde questioned what lays, bydding hym syng the same, and saying hee knew but of two lays: " 'Twas yn Trafalgar's bay wee saw the Frenchmen lay," and "There wee lay all that day yn the Bay of Biscay-O," whych hee forthwyth hummed aloud, yet out of tune, at whych somme smyled.

Witness continued: "that hee perchaunce coulde chaunt the sayde lays wyth Music, but unaccompanied hee durst not." On thys they hadde hym to the Schoolroom, where was a Musical Instrument, called a Paean-o-Forty, (meaning that yt hadde forty Notes, and was a Paean or Triumph or Art,) whereon two young ladyes, Nieces of my Loorde, that abode there, (lerning, as they deemed, Lessons; but, I wot, idlynge not a lyttle,) did wyth much thumpyng playe certyn Music wyth hys synging, as best they mighte, seeing that the Tunes were such as noe Man had herde before.

> Lorenzo dwelt at Heighington,
>   (Hys cote was made of Dimity,)
> Least-ways yf not exactly there,
>   Yet yn yts close proximity.
> Hee called on mee—hee stayed to tee—
>   Yet not a word hee ut-tered,
> Untyl I sayd, "D'ye lyke your bread
>   Dry?" and hee answered "But-tered."

(Chorus whereyn all present joyned with fervour.)

> Noodle dumb
> Has a noodle-head,
> I hate such noodles, *I* do.

Witness continued: "that shee then appeared unto hym habited yn the same loose Wrapper, whereyn hee first saw her yn hys Dreem, and yn a stayd and piercing tone gave forth her History as followeth."

The Ladye's History

"On a dewie autumn evening, mighte have been seen, pacing yn the grounds harde by Aucklande Castell, a yong Ladye of a stiff and perky manner, yet not ill to look on, nay, one mighte saye, faire to a degree, save that haply that hadde been untrue.

"That yong Ladye, O miserable Man, was I" (whereon I demanded on what score shee held mee miserable, and shee replied, yt mattered not.) "I plumed myself yn those tymes on my exceeding not soe much beauty as loftiness of Figure, and gretely desired that some Painter might paint my picture; but they ever were too high, not yn skyll I trow, but yn charges." (At thys I most humbly enquired at what charge the then Painters wrought, but shee loftily affirmed that money-matters were vulgar and that she knew not, no, nor cared.)

"Now yt chaunced that a certyn Artist, hight Lorenzo, came toe that Quarter, having wyth hym a merveillous machine called by men a Chimera (that ys, a fabulous and wholy incredible thing;) where wyth hee took manie pictures, each yn a single stroke of Tyme, whiles that a Man might name 'John, the son of Robin' (I asked her, what might a stroke of Tyme bee, but shee, frowning, answered not).

"He yt was that undertook my Picture: yn which I mainly required one thyng, that yt shoulde bee at full-length, for yn none other way mighte my Loftiness bee trulie set forth. Nevertheless, though hee took manie Pictures, yet all fayled yn thys: for some, beginning at the Hedde reeched not toe the Feet; others, takyng yn the Feet, yet left out the Hedde; whereof the former were a grief unto myself, and the latter a Laughing-Stocke unto others.

"At these thyngs I justly fumed, having at the first been frendly unto hym (though yn sooth hee was dull), and oft smote hym gretely on the Eares, rending from hys Hedde certyn Locks, whereat crying out hee was wont toe saye that I made hys lyfe a burden untoe hym, whych thyng I not so much doubted as highlie rejoyced yn.

"At the last hee counselled thys, that a Picture shoulde bee made, showing so much skyrt as mighte reasonably bee gotte yn, and a

78

Notice set below toe thys effect: 'Item, two yards and a Half Ditto, and then the Feet.' Byt thys no Whit contented mee, and thereon I shut hym ynto the Cellar, where hee remaned three Weeks, growing dayly thinner and thinner, till at the last hee floted up and downe like a Feather.

"Now yt fell at thys tyme, as I questioned hym on a certyn Day, yf hee woulde nowe take mee at full-length, and hee replying untoe mee, yn a little moning Voyce, lyke a Gnat, one chaunced to open the Door: whereat the Draft bore hym uppe ynto a Cracke of the Cieling, and I remaned awaytyng hym, holding uppe my Torche, until such time as I also faded ynto a Ghost, yet stickyng untoe the Wall."

Then did my Loorde and the Companie haste down ynto the Cellar, for to see thys straunge sight, to whych place when they came, my Loorde bravely drew hys sword, loudly crying "Death!" (though to whom or what he explained not); then some went yn, but the more part hung back, urging on those yn front, not soe largely bye example, as Words of cheer; yet at last all entered, my Loorde last.

Then they removed from the wall the Casks and other stuff, and founde the sayd Ghost, dredful toe relate, yet extant on the Wall, at which horrid sight such screems were raysed as yn these days are seldom or never herde; some faynted, others bye large drafts of Beer saved themselves from that Extremity, yet were they scarcely alive for Feer.

Then dyd the Layde speak unto them yn suchwise:

"Here I bee, and here I byde,
Till such tyme as yt betyde
That a Ladye of thys place,
Lyke to mee yn name and face,
(Though my name bee never known,
My initials shall bee shown,)

79

Shall be fotograffed aright—
Hedde and Feet bee both yn sight—
Then my face shall disappear,
Nor agayn affrite you heer."

Then sayd Matthew Dixon unto her, "Wherefore holdest thou
uppe that Torche?" to whych shee answered, "Candles Gyve
Light": but none understood her.

After thys a thyn Voyce sayd from overhedde:

"Yn the Auckland Castell cellar,
Long, long ago,
I was shut—a brisk young feller—
Woe, woe, ah woe!
To take her at full-lengthe
I never hadde the strengthe
Tempore (and soe I tell her)
Practerito!"

(Yn thys Chorus they durst none joyn, seeing that Latyn was
untoe them a Tongue unknown.)

"She was hard—oh, she was cruel—
Long, long ago,
Starved mee here—not even gruel—
No, believe mee, no!—
Frae Scotland could I flee,
I'd gie my last bawbee,—
Arrah, bhoys, fair play's a jhewel,
Lave me, darlints, goe!"

Then my Loorde, putting bye hys Sworde, (whych was layd
up thereafter, yn memory of soe grete Bravery,) bade hys Butler
fetch hym presentlie a Vessel of Beer, whych when yt was brought
at hys nod, (nor, as hee merrily sayd, hys "nod, and Bec, and
wreathed smyle,") hee drank hugelie thereof: "for why?" quoth
hee, "surely a Bec ys no longer a Bec, when yt ys Dry."

PHOTOGRAPHY EXTRAORDINARY

(From "The Rectory Umbrella")

The recent extraordinary discovery in Photography, as applied to the operations of the mind, has reduced the art of novel-writing to the merest mechanical labour. We have been kindly permitted by the artist to be present during one of his experiments; but as the invention has not yet been given to the world, we are only at liberty to relate the results, suppressing all details of chemicals and manipulation.

The operator began by stating that the ideas of the feeblest intellect, when once received on properly prepared paper, could be "developed" up to any required degree of intensity. On hearing our wish that he would begin with an extreme case, he obligingly summoned a young man from an adjoining room, who appeared to be of the very weakest possible physical and mental powers. On being asked what we thought of him we candidly confessed that he seemed incapable of anything but sleep; our friend cordially assented to this opinion.

The machine being in position, and a mesmeric rapport established between the mind of the patient and the object glass, the young man was asked whether he wished to say anything; he feebly replied "Nothing." He was then asked what he was thinking of, and the answer, as before, was "Nothing." The artist on this pronounced him to be in a most satisfactory state, and at once commenced the operation.

After the paper had been exposed for the requisite time, it was removed and submitted to our inspection; we found it to be covered

81

with faint and almost illegible characters. A closer scrutiny revealed the following:

"The eve was soft and dewy mild; a zephyr whispered in the

lofty glade, and a few light drops of rain cooled the thirsty soil. At a slow amble, along the primrose-bordered path rode a gentle-looking and amiable youth, holding a light cane in his delicate hand; the pony moved gracefully beneath him, inhaling as it went the fragrance of the roadside flowers; the calm smile, and languid eyes, so admirably harmonising with the fair features of the rider, showed the even tenor of his thoughts. With a sweet though feeble voice, he plaintively murmured out the gentle regrets that clouded his breast:

'Alas! she would not hear my prayer!
Yet it were rash to tear my hair;
Disfigured, I should be less fair.

82

'She was unwise, I may say blind;
Once she was lovingly inclined;
Some circumstance has changed her mind.'

There was a moment's silence; the pony stumbled over a stone in the path, and unseated his rider. A crash was heard among the dried leaves; the youth arose; a slight bruise on his left shoulder, and a disarrangement of his cravat, were the only traces that remained of this trifling accident."

"This," we remarked, as we returned the paper, "belongs apparently to the milk-and-water School of Novels."

"You are quite right," our friend replied, "and, in its present state, it is, of course, utterly unsaleable in the present day: we shall find, however, that the next stage of development will remove it into the strong-minded or Matter-of-Fact School." After dipping it into various acids, he again submitted it to us: it had now become the following:

"The evening was of the ordinary character, barometer at 'change'; a wind was getting up in the wood, and some rain was beginning to fall; a bad look-out for the farmers. A gentleman approached along the bridle-road, carrying a stout knobbed stick in his hand, and mounted on a serviceable nag, possibly worth some £40 or so; there was a settled business-like expression on the rider's face, and he whistled as he rode; he seemed to be hunting for rhymes in his head, and at length repeated, in a satisfied tone, the following composition:

'Well! so my offer was no go!
She might do worse, I told her so;
She was a fool to answer "No."

'However, things are as they stood;
Nor would I have her if I could,
For there are plenty more as good.'

83

At this moment the horse set his foot in a hole, and rolled over; his rider rose with difficulty; he had sustained several severe bruises and fractured two ribs; it was some time before he forgot that unlucky day."

We returned this with the strongest expression of admiration, and requested that it might now be developed to the highest possible degree. Our friend readily consented, and shortly presented us with the result, which he informed us belonged to the Spasmodic or German School. We perused it with indescribable sensations of surprise and delight:

"The night was wildly tempestuous—a hurricane raved through the murky forest—furious torrents of rain lashed the groaning earth. With a headling rush—down a precipitous mountain gorge —dashed a mounted horseman armed to the teeth—his horse bounded beneath him at a mad gallop, snorting fire from its distended nostrils as it flew. The rider's knotted brows—rolling eyeballs—and clenched teeth—expressed the intense agony of his mind —weird visions loomed upon his burning brain—while with a mad yell he poured forth the torrent of his boiling passion:

'Firebrands and daggers! hope hath fled!
To atoms dash the doubly dead!
My brain is fire—my heart is lead!

'Her soul is flint, and what am I?
Scorch'd by her fierce, relentless eye,
Nothingness is my destiny!'

There was a moment's pause. Horror! his path ended in a fathomless abyss. . . . A rush—a flash—a crash—all was over. Three drops of blood, two teeth, and a stirrup were all that remained to tell where the wild horseman met his doom."

The young man was now recalled to consciousness, and shown the result of the workings of his mind; he instantly fainted away.

Photography Extraordinary

In the present infancy of the art we forbear from further comment on this wonderful discovery; but the mind reels as it contemplates the stupendous addition thus made to the powers of science.

Our friend concluded with various minor experiments, such as working up a passage of Wordsworth into strong, sterling poetry: the same experiment was tried on a passage of Byron, at our request, but the paper came out scorched and blistered all over by the fiery epithets thus produced.

As a concluding remark: *could* this art be applied (we put the question in the strictest confidence)—*could* it, we ask, be applied to the speeches in Parliament? It may be but a delusion of our heated imagination, but we will still cling fondly to the idea, and hope against hope.

HINTS FOR ETIQUETTE; OR, DINING OUT MADE EASY

(From "The Rectory Umbrella")

As caterers for the public taste, we can conscientiously recommend this book to all diners-out who are perfectly unacquainted with the usages of society. However we may regret that our author has confined himself to warning rather than advice, we are bound in justice to say that nothing here stated will be found to contradict the habits of the best circles. The following examples exhibit a depth of penetration and a fullness of experience rarely met with:

I

In proceeding to the dining-room, the gentleman gives one arm to the lady he escorts—it is unusual to offer both.

II

The practice of taking soup with the next gentleman but one is now wisely discontinued; but the custom of asking your host his opinion of the weather immediately on the removal of the first course still prevails.

III

To use a fork with your soup, intimating at the same time to your hostess that you are reserving the spoon for the beefsteaks, is a practice wholly exploded.

IV

On meat being placed before you, there is no possible objection to your eating it, if so disposed; still, in all such delicate cases, be guided entirely by the conduct of those around you.

V

It is always allowable to ask for artichoke jelly with your boiled venison; however, there are houses where this is not supplied.

VI

The method of helping roast turkey with two carving-forks is practicable, but deficient in grace.

VII

We do not recommend the practice of eating cheese with a knife and fork in one hand, and a spoon and wine-glass in the other; there is a kind of awkwardness in the action which no amount of practice can entirely dispel.

VIII

As a general rule, do not kick the shins of the opposite gentleman under the table, if personally unacquainted with him; your pleasantry is liable to be misunderstood—a circumstance at all times unpleasant.

IX

Proposing the health of the boy in buttons immediately on the removal of the cloth is a custom springing from regard to his tender years, rather than from a strict adherence to the rules of etiquette.

A HEMISPHERICAL PROBLEM

(From "The Rectory Umbrella")

Half of the world, or nearly so, is always in the light of the sun: as the world turns round, this hemisphere of light shifts round too, and passes over each part of it in succession.

Supposing on Tuesday, it is morning at London; in another hour it would be Tuesday morning at the west of England; if the whole world were land we might go on tracing * Tuesday morning, Tuesday morning all the way round, till in twenty-four hours we get to London again. But we *know* that at London twenty-four hours after Tuesday morning it is Wednesday morning. Where, then, in its passage round the earth, does the day change its name? Where does it lose its identity?

Practically there is no difficulty in it, because a great part of the journey is over water, and what it does out at sea no one can tell: and besides there are so many different languages that it would be hopeless to attempt to trace the name of any one day all the year round. But is the case inconceivable that the same land and the same language should continue all round the world? I cannot see that it is: in that case either † there would be no distinction at all between each successive day, and so week, month, etc., so that we should have to say, "The Battle of Waterloo happened to-day, about

---

* The best way is to imagine yourself walking round with the sun and asking the inhabitants as you go, "What morning is this?" If you suppose them living all the way around, and all speaking one language, the difficulty is obvious.

† This is clearly an impossible case, and is only put as an hypothesis.

89

two million hours ago," or some line would have to be fixed where the change should take place, so that the inhabitants of one house would wake and say, "Heigh-ho, * Tuesday morning!" and the inhabitants of the next (over the line), a few miles to the west would wake a few minutes afterwards and say, "Heigh-ho! Wednesday morning!" What hopeless confusion the people who happened to live *on* the line would be in, is not for me to say. There would be a quarrel every morning as to what the name of the day should be. I can imagine no third case, unless everybody was allowed to choose for themselves, which state of things would be rather worse than either of the other two.

I am aware that this idea has been started before—namely, by the unknown author of that beautiful poem beginning, "If all the world were apple pie," etc. † The particular result here discussed, however, does not appear to have occurred to him, as he confines himself to the difficulties in obtaining drink which would certainly ensue.

* The usual exclamation at waking, generally said with a yawn.

† "If all the world were apple pie,
    And all the sea were ink,
And all the trees were bread and cheese,
    What *should* we have to drink?"

THE IDEAL MATHEMATICAL SCHOOL *

(From "Notes by an Oxford Chiel," 1871)

It has occurred to me to suggest for consideration how desirable roofed buildings are for carrying on mathematical calculations: in fact, the variable character of the weather in Oxford renders it highly inexpedient to attempt much occupation, of a sedentary nature, in the open air. Again, it is often impossible to carry on accurate mathematical calculations in close contiguity to one another, owing to their mutual conversation; consequently, these processes require different rooms in which irrepressible conversationalists, who arc found to occur in every branch of Society, might be carefully and permanently fixed.

It may be sufficient for the present to enumerate the following requisites—others might be added as funds permit:

A. A very large room for calculating Greatest Common Measure. To this a small one might be added for Least Common Multiple: this, however, might be dispensed with.

B. A piece of open ground for keeping Roots and practising their extraction: it would be advisable to keep Square Roots by themselves, as their corners are apt to damage others.

C. A room for reducing Fractions to their Lowest Terms. This should be provided with a cellar for keeping the Lowest Terms when found, which might also be available to the general body of Undergraduates, for the purpose of "keeping Terms."

* This whimsical skit burlesques the contents of a letter in which the Professor of Physics at Christ Church met an offer of the Clarendon Trustees by a detailed enumeration of the requirements in his own department of Natural Science.

D.   A large room, which might be darkened, and fitted up with a magic lantern, for the purpose of exhibiting circulating Decimals in the act of circulation.   This might also contain cupboards, fitted with glass doors, for keeping the various Scales of Notation.

E.   A narrow strip of ground, railed off and carefully levelled, for investigating the properties of Asymptotes, and testing practically whether Parallel Lines meet or not: for this purpose it should reach, to use the expressive language of Euclid, "ever so far."

This last process of "continually producing the lines" may require centuries or more, but such a period, though long in the life of an individual, is as nothing in the life of the University.

As Photography is now very much employed in recording human expressions, and might possibly be adapted to Algebraical Expressions, a small photographic room would be desirable, both for general use and for representing the various phenomena of Gravity, Disturbance of Equilibrium, Resolution, etc., which affect the features during severe mathematical operations.

LOVE AND LOCI *

(A Mathematical Courtship)

It was a lovely Autumn evening, and the glorious effects of chromatic aberration were beginning to show themselves in the atmosphere as the earth revolved away from the great western luminary, when two lines might have been observed wending their weary way across a plain superficies. The elder of the two had, by long practice, acquired the art, so painful to young and impulsive loci, of lying evenly between her extreme points; but the younger, in her girlish impetuosity, was ever longing to diverge and become an hyperbola or some such romantic and boundless curve.

"They had lived and loved: fate and the intervening superficies had hitherto kept them asunder, but this was no longer to be: *a line had intersected them, making the two interior angles together less than two right angles.* It was a moment never to be forgotten and they journeyed on, a whisper thrilled along the superficies in isochronous waves of sound, 'Yes! We shall at length meet, if continually produced!'" ("Jacobi's Course of Mathematics," Chap. I.). We have commenced with the above quotation as a striking illustration of the advantage of introducing the human element into the hitherto barren region of Mathematics. Who shall say what germs of romance, hitherto not observed, may not underlie the subject? Who can tell whether the parallelogram, which in our ignorance we have defined and drawn, and the whole of whose properties we profess to know, may not be all the while

* From "The Dynamics of a Parti-cle" (1865).

95

panting for exterior angles, sympathetic with the interior, or sullenly repining at the fact that it cannot be inscribed in a circle?

What mathematician has ever pondered over an hyperbola, mangling the unfortunate curve with lines of intersection here and there, in his efforts to prove some property that perhaps after all is a mere calumny, who has not fancied at last that the ill-used locus was spreading out its asymptotes as a silent rebuke, or winking one focus at him in contemptuous pity?

MORNING DRESS AND EVENING DRESS *

Surely, if you go to morning parties in evening dress (which you *do*, you know), why not to evening parties in morning dress?

You will say, "What morning parties do I go to in evening dress?"

I reply, "Balls—most balls go on in the morning."

Anyhow, I have been invited to three evening parties in London this year, in each of which "Morning Dress" was specified.

Again, doctors (not that I am a real one—only an amateur) must always be in trim for an instant summons to a patient. And when you invite a doctor to dinner (say), do you not always add "Morning Dress"? (I grant you it is done by initials in *this* case. And perhaps you will say you don't understand M.D. to stand for "Morning Dress"? Then take a few lessons in elementary spelling.) Aye, and many and many a time have I received invitations to evening parties wherein the actual colours of the Morning Dress expected were stated!

For instance, "Red Scarf: Vest, Pink." That is a *very* common form, though it is usually (I grant you) expressed by initials.

*From a letter to Miss Dora Abdy (1880).

KISSING BY POST *

This really will *not* do, you know, sending one more kiss every time by post: the parcel gets so heavy it is quite expensive. When the postman brought in the last letter, he looked quite grave. "Two pounds to pay, sir!" he said. *"Extra weight, sir!"* (I think he

cheats a little, by the way. He often makes me pay two *pounds*, when I think it should be *pence*.)

* From letters written in 1875 and 1876 to Gertrude Chataway, a little child whom he met at Sandown, Isle of Wight, and to whom he dedicated "The Hunting of the Snark."

"Oh, if you please, Mr. Postman!" I said, going down gracefully on one knee (I wish you could see me going down on one knee to a postman—it's a very pretty sight), "do excuse me just this once ! It's only from a little girl!"

"Only from a little girl!" he growled. "What are little girls made of?" "Sugar and spice," I began to say, "and all that's ni——," but he interrupted me. "No! I don't mean *that*. I mean, what's the good of little girls when they send such heavy letters?" "Well, they're not *much* good, certainly," I said, rather sadly.

"Mind you don't get any more such letters," he said, "at least, not from that particular little girl. *I know her well, and she's a regular bad one!*"

That's not true, is it? I don't believe he ever saw you, and you're not a bad one, are you? However, I promised him we would send each other *very* few more letters. "Only two thousand four hundred and seventy, or so," I said. "Oh!" said he, "a little number like *that* doesn't signify. What I meant is, you mustn't send *many*."

So you see we must keep count now, and when we get to two thousand four hundred and seventy, we mustn't write any more, unless the postman gives us leave.

You will be sorry, and surprised, and puzzled, to hear what a queer illness I have had ever since you went. I sent for the doctor, and said, "Give me some medicine, for I'm tired." He said, "Nonsense and stuff! You don't want medicine: go to bed!" I said, "No; it isn't the sort of tiredness that wants bed. I'm tired in the *face*." He looked a little grave, and said, "Oh, it's your *nose* that's tired: a person often talks too much when he thinks he nose a great deal." I said, "No it isn't the nose. Perhaps it's the *hair*." Then he looked grave and said, "*Now* I understand: you've been playing too many hairs on the piano-forte." "No, indeed I haven't!" I said, "and it isn't exactly the *hair*: it's more about the nose and the

99

chin." Then he looked a good deal graver, and said "Have you been walking much on your chin, lately?" I said, "No." "Well!" he said, "it puzzles me very much. Do you think that it's in the lips?"

"Of course!" I said, "that's exactly what it is!" Then he looked very grave indeed, and said, "I think you must have been giving too many kisses." "Well," I said, "I did give *one* kiss to a baby child, a little friend of mine." "Think again," he said, "are you sure it was only *one?*" I thought again, and said, "Perhaps it was eleven times." Then the doctor said, "You must not give her *any* more till your lips are quite rested again." "But what am I to do?" I said, "because, you see, I owe her a hundred and eighty-two more." Then he looked so grave that the tears ran down his cheeks, and he said, "You may send them to her in a box."

Then I remembered a little box that I once bought at Dover, and thought I would some day give it to some little girl or other. So I have packed them all in it very carefully. Tell me if they come safe or if any are lost on the way.

MY STYLE OF DANCING *

As to dancing, I *never* dance, unless I am allowed to do it *in my own peculiar way*. There is no use trying to describe it: it has to be seen to be believed. The last house I tried it in, the floor broke through. But then it was a poor sort of floor—the beams were only

six inches thick, hardly worth calling beams at all: stone arches are much more sensible, when any dancing, *of my peculiar kind*, is to be done.

Did you ever see the Rhinoceros and the Hippopotamus, at the Zoological Gardens, trying to dance a minuet together? It is a touching sight.

* From a letter, written in 1873, to Gayner Simpson, a child friend at Guildford.

GLOVES FOR KITTENS *

Oh, you naughty, naughty little culprit!

If only I could fly to Fulham with a handy little stick (ten feet long and four inches thick is my favourite size) how I would rap your wicked little knuckles. However, there isn't much harm done, so I will sentence you to a very mild punishment—only one year's imprisonment. If you'll just tell the Fulham policeman about it, he'll manage all the rest for you, and he'll fit you with a nice comfortable pair of handcuffs, and lock you up in a nice cosy dark cell, and feed you on nice dry bread and delicious cold water.

But how badly you *do* spell your words! I *was* so puzzled about the "sack full of love and basket full of kisses!" But at last I made out why, of course, you meant "a sack full of *gloves*, and a basket full of *kittens!*"

Then I understood what you were sending me. And just then Mrs. Dyer came to tell me a large sack and a basket had come. There was such a miawing in the house, as if all the cats in Eastbourne had come to see me!

"Oh, just open them please, Mrs. Dyer, and count the things in them."

So in a few minutes Mrs. Dyer came and said "500 pairs of gloves in the sack and 250 kittens in the basket."

"Dear me! That makes 1,000 gloves! four times as many gloves as kittens! It's very kind of Maggie, but why did she send so many gloves? for I haven't got 1,000 *hands*, you know, Mrs. Dyer."

---

* This whimsical and characteristic paper, which has never been published before, is from a letter written by Lewis Carroll on September 17, 1893, from 7, Lushington Road, Eastbourne, to Miss Maggie Bowman.

And Mrs. Dyer said, "No, indeed, you're 998 hands short of that."

However, the next day I made out what to do, and I took the basket with me and walked off to the parish school—the *girls'* school, you know—and I said to the mistress:

"How many little girls are there at school to-day?"

"Exactly 250, sir."

"And have they all been *very* good, all day?"

"As good as gold, sir."

I waited outside the door with my basket, and as each little girl came out, I just popped a soft little kitten into her hands! Oh! what joy there was! The little girls went all dancing home, nursing their kittens, and the whole air was full of purring! Then, the next morning, I went to the school, before it opened, to ask the little girls how the kittens had behaved in the night. And they all arrived sobbing and crying, and their faces and hands were all covered with scratches, and they had the kittens wrapped up in their pinafores to keep them from scratching any more. And they sobbed out, "The kittens have been scratching us all night, all the night!"

So then I said to myself, "What a nice little girl Maggie is. *Now* I see why she sent all those gloves, and why there are four times as many gloves as kittens! And I said to the little girls, "Never mind, my dear children, do your lessons *very* nicely, and don't cry any more, and when school is over, you'll find me at the door, and you shall see what you shall see!"

So, in the evening, when the little girls came running out, with the kittens still wrapped up in their pinafores, there was I, at the door, with a big sack! And, as each little girl came out, I just popped into her hand two pairs of gloves! And each little girl unrolled her pinafore and took out an angry little kitten, spitting and snarling, with its claws sticking out like a hedgehog.

But it hadn't time to scratch for, in one moment, it found all its four claws popped into nice soft warm gloves! And then the kittens got quite sweet-tempered and gentle, and began purring again.

So the little girls went dancing home again, and the next morning they came dancing back to school. The scratches were all healed, and they told me "The kittens *have* been good!"

"And when any kitten wants to catch a mouse, it just takes off *one* of its gloves; and if it wants to catch two mice; it takes off *two* gloves; and if it wants to catch *three* mice, it takes off *three* gloves; and if it wants to catch *four* mice, it takes off all its gloves. But the moment they've caught the mice, they pop their gloves on again, because they know we can't love them without their gloves. For, you see, 'gloves' have got 'love' *inside* them—there's none outside."

So all the little girls said, "Please thank Maggie, and we send her 250 *loves* and 1,000 kisses in return for her 250 kittens and her 1,000 gloves!"

Your loving old Uncle,
C. L. D.

Love and kisses to Nellie and Emsie.

ART IN POTSDAM *

The amount of art lavished on the whole region of Potsdam is marvellous; some of the tops of the palaces were like forests of statues, and they were all over the gardens, set on pedestals. In fact, the two principles of Berlin architecture appear to me to be these. On the house-tops, wherever there is a convenient place, put up the figure of a man; he is best placed standing on one leg. Wherever there is room on the ground, put either a circular group of busts on pedestals, in consultation, all looking inwards—or else the colossal figure of a man killing, about to kill, or having killed (the present tense is preferred) a beast; the more pricks the beast has, the better—in fact, a dragon is the correct thing, but if that is beyond the artist, he may content himself with a lion or a pig. The beast-killing principle has been carried out everywhere with a relentless monotony, which makes some parts of Berlin look like a fossil slaughter-house.

* This extract from Lewis Carroll's diary, written during his Continental tour with Dr. Liddon in 1867, although obviously not coming within the category of "Nonsense," is so sprightly and so whimsically apposite that the editor has ventured to include it in this volume as a characteristic fragment of Lewis Carroll's humour that ought to be preserved.

ON WAITERS

(Extracts from Mr. Dodgson's diary during his Continental tour with
Canon Liddon in the summer of 1867)

July 13th (Dover). We breakfasted, as agreed, at eight, or at
least we then sat down and nibbled bread and butter till such time
as the chops could be done, which great event took place at half-
past. We tried pathetic appeals to the wandering waiters, who told
us, "They are coming, sir," in a soothing tone, and we tried stern
remonstrance, and they then said, "They are coming, sir," in a more
injured tone; and after all such appeals they retired into their dens,
and hid themselves behind sideboards and dish-covers, and still the
chops came not. We agreed that of all virtues a waiter can display,
that of a retiring disposition is quite the least desirable.

August 6th (Nijni Novgorod). We went to the Smernovaya
(or some such name) Hotel, a truly villainous place, though no
doubt the best in the town. The feeding was very good and every-
thing else very bad. It was some consolation to find that as we sat
at dinner we furnished a subject of the liveliest interest to six or
seven waiters, all dressed in white tunics, belted at the waist, and
white trousers, who ranged themselves in a row and gazed in a quite
absorbed way at the collection of strange animals that were feeding
before them. Now and then a twinge of conscience would seize
them that they were, after all, not fulfilling the great object of life
as waiters, and on these occasions they would all hurry to the end of
the room, and refer to a great drawer which seemed to contain nothing but spoons and corks. When we asked for anything, they first

looked at each other in an alarmed way; then, when they had ascertained which understood the order best, they all followed his example, which always was to refer to the big drawer.

September 4th (Giessen). We moved on to Giessen, and put up at the "Rappe Hotel" for the night, and ordered an early breakfast of an obliging waiter who talked English. "Coffee!" he exclaimed delightedly, catching at the word as if it were a really original idea. "Ah, coffee—very nice—and eggs? Ham with your eggs? Very nice——" "If we can have it broiled," I said.

"Boiled?" the waiter repeated with an incredulous smile.

"No, not *boiled*," I explained—"*broiled!*" The waiter put aside this distinction as trivial. "Yes, yes, ham," he repeated, reverting to his favourite idea. "Yes, ham," I said, "but how cooked?"

"Yes, yes, how cooked," the waiter replied with the careless air of one who assents to a proposition more from good nature than from a real conviction of its truth.

LEWIS CARROLL AS A RACONTEUR *

An old lady I knew, once tried to check the military ardour of a little boy by showing him the picture of a battlefield and describing some of its horrors. But the only reply she got was, "I'll be a soldier. Tell it again!"

*   *   *   *   *

Another little boy, after having listened with great attention to the story of Lot's wife, asked innocently, "Where does the salt come from that's not made of ladies?"

*   *   *   *   *

Dr. Paget (Dean of Christ Church) was conducting a school examination, and in the course of his questions he happened to ask a small boy the meaning of "average." He was utterly bewildered by the reply, "The things that hens lay on," until the youngster explained that he had read in a book that hens lay *on an average* so many eggs a year!

* No book of this kind would be comprehensive without reference to Lewis Carroll's inimitable talent as a raconteur. Stored within his mind were numberless entertaining anecdotes, some true, some invented by himself, and some he had heard. As a matter of fact, he had heard so many that he was a difficult man to tell a story to—it was sure to be familiar to him. In selecting for reproduction some of the best Lewis Carroll anecdotes —both *by* him and *about* him—the editor has ventured to include several which do not come within the category of "Nonsense," but trusts that their interest will excuse this deviation from the professed plan of this work. It is recorded that Mr. Carroll (or Mr. Dodgson, to be strictly accurate when dealing with this characteristic) was an excellent after-dinner speaker, and told stories exceedingly well with an effective stutter reminiscent of Charles Lamb.

113

Have you heard the story of the dog who was sent into the sea after sticks? He brought them back properly for a time, and then returned swimming in a curious manner, and apparently in difficulties. On closer inspection it appeared that he had caught hold of his own tail in mistake and was bringing it to land in triumph!

*   *   *   *   *

On one occasion I was walking in Oxford with Maggie Bowman,* then a mere child, when we met the Bishop of Oxford, to whom I introduced my little guest. His lordship asked her what she thought of Oxford, and was much amused when the little actress replied, with true professional aplomb, "I think it's the best place in the provinces!"

THREE STORIES FROM MR. DODGSON'S DIARY

July 23, 1867 (when on holiday in Dantzig). On our way to the station we came across the grandest instance of the "Majesty of Justice" that I have ever witnessed. A little boy was being taken to the magistrate, or to prison (probably for picking a pocket). The achievement of this feat had been entrusted to two soldiers in full uniform, who were solemnly marching, one in front of the poor little urchin and one behind, with bayonets fixed, of course, to be ready to charge in case he should attempt to escape.

August, 1867 (on a visit to Kronstadt with Canon Liddon, of Oxford). Liddon had surrendered his overcoat early in the day, and we found it must be recovered from the waiting-maid, who talked only Russian, and as I had left the dictionary behind, and the little vocabulary did not contain *coat*, we were in some difficulty. Liddon began by exhibiting his coat, with much gesticulation, in-

* Sister of Isa who so charmingly played the heroine in the stage version of "Alice," after Miss Phœbe Carlo. The Bowman sisters were among the most intimate of Lewis Carroll's friends.

cluding the taking it half off. To our delight, she appeared to understand at once, left the room, and returned in a minute with— a large clothes brush. On this Liddon tried a further and more energetic demonstration; he took off his coat and laid it at her feet, pointed downwards (to intimate that in the lower regions was the object of his desire), smiled with an expression of the joy and gratitude with which he would receive it, and put the coat on again. Once more a gleam of intelligence lighted up the plain but expressive features of the young person; she was absent much longer this time, and when she returned, she brought, to our dismay, a large cushion and a pillow, and began to prepare the sofa for the nap that she now saw clearly was the thing the dumb gentleman wanted. A happy thought occurred to me, and I hastily drew a sketch representing Liddon, with one coat on, receiving a second and larger one from the hands of a benignant Russian peasant. The language of hieroglyphics succeeded where all other means had failed, and we returned to St. Petersburg with the humiliating knowledge that our standard of civilisation was now reduced to the level of ancient Nineveh.

December 17, 1895. I have given books to Kate Tyndall and Sydney Fairbrother, and have heard from them, and find I was entirely mistaken in taking them for children. Both are married women! *

*   *   *   *   *

Lewis Carroll had a nervous horror of infection that occasionally resulted in a good deal of unconscious humour. During a brief holiday which the two elder Miss Bowmans spent with him at East-

---

* In an earlier entry in the diary Mr. Dodgson refers to the clever acting of "Kate Tyndall and Sydney Fairbrother, whom I guess to be about fifteen and twelve," in the sensational melodrama "Two Little Vagabonds" at the Princess's Theatre.

bourne, the news came that their youngest sister had caught scarlet fever. After this, the two children had to read every letter which came from their mother as best they could from the other side of the room, while their host held the epistle aloft, his head averted so that he should not see what was not intended for his eyes.

*   *   *   *   *

On the occasion of another Eastbourne visit the same little girls were taken by their friend for a steamer trip to Hastings. This was with the idea of accustoming them to sea-travelling, in view of the forthcoming professional visit of the little actresses to America. Their "rehearsal" was certainly instructive, for the sea was much rougher than at any time during their subsequent trip across the Atlantic, with the result that they suffered considerably. "Uncle Dodgson," as they invariably called him, did his best to console them by continually repeating, "Crossing the Atlantic will be much worse than this!"

*   *   *   *   *

He (Lewis Carroll) had a wonderfully good memory, except for faces and dates. The former were always a stumbling block to him, and people used to say (most unjustly) that he was intention-ally short-sighted. One night he went up to London to dine with a friend, whom he had only recently met. The next morning a gentleman greeted him as he was walking.

"I beg your pardon," said Mr. Dodgson, "but you have the ad-vantage of me. I have no remembrance of having ever seen you before this moment."

"That is very strange," the other replied, "for I was your host last night!"

*   *   *   *   *

Tight boots were a great aversion of his, especially for children. One little girl who was staying with him at Eastbourne had occasion to buy a new pair of boots. Lewis Carroll gave instructions to the

116

bootmaker as to how they were to be made, so as to be thoroughly comfortable, with the result that when they came home they were more useful than ornamental, being very nearly as broad as they were long! Which shows that even hygienic principles may be pushed too far.

      *   *   *   *   *

In Guildford there is (or was) an American confectioner's, where the cakes are cooked by a very quick process before the public and handed to you smoking hot, direct from the cook. This preparation used to be a source of considerable interest to the juvenile population, who could watch the proceedings through the shop window. One afternoon, when Lewis Carroll was purchasing cakes for some of his child chums, seven small ragged youngsters formed an envious group outside. But they soon became a participatory one, for, purchasing seven of the choicest specimens of confectionery, the lover of children took them outside and distributed them to the eager little ones.

      *   *   *   *   *

"My first introduction" * (writes Sir George Baden-Powell) "to the author of 'Through the Looking Glass' was about the year 1870 or 1871, and under appropriate conditions! I was then coaching at Oxford with the well-known Rev. E. Hatch, and was on friendly terms with his bright and pretty children. Entering his house one day, and facing the dining-room, I heard mysterious noises under the table, and saw the cloth move as if some one were hiding. Children's legs revealed it as no burglar, and there was nothing for it but to crawl upon them, roaring as a lion. Bursting in upon them, in their stronghold under the table, I was met by the staid but amused gaze of a reverend gentleman. Frequently afterwards did

    *This and the two succeeding anecdotes are from "The Life and Letters of Lewis Carroll."

I see and hear Lewis Carroll entertaining the youngsters in his inimitable way."

Possibly the funniest story about Lewis Carroll is the rather well-known one which relates how Queen Victoria, being charmed by "Alice in Wonderland," and hearing that the author was really the Rev. C. L. Dodgson, ordered the rest of his works. Her surprise at receiving a large parcel of mathematical and technical works may be imagined!